THE DAY
JESSE JAMES WAS KILLED

April 3, 1882, St. Joseph, Missouri. The sun rose at 6:10 A.M. Temperature: 44 degrees. Barometer: 30.74. The wind was from the southeast. It was a Monday. . . .

The world was in flux. The United States of America was straining at the seams, bursting with growth and progress. But there was no place for Jesse in this new world. He realized this and it troubled him. His two worst enemies were gnawing at him—time and himself. He was a misfit. There were only three roads to the future. Death, imprisonment, or ridicule. There is no place in the world for a tame desperado.

Jesse was an old-young man of thirty-four, and he was about to die. . . .

More Westerns from SIGNET

THE DAY JESSE JAMES WAS KILLED

BY

CARL W. BREIHAN

Ⓞ
A SIGNET BOOK
NEW AMERICAN LIBRARY
TIMES MIRROR

DEDICATED TO
ROBERT REDFORD AND PAUL NEWMAN
WHOSE PORTRAYALS OF BUTCH
CASSIDY AND THE SUNDANCE
KID HAVE THRILLED
MILLIONS

Copyright © 1961, 1979 by Carl W. Breihan

Library of Congress Catalog Card Number: 60-14982

SIGNET TRADEMARK REG. U.S. PAT. OFF. AND FOREIGN COUNTRIES
REGISTERED TRADEMARK—MARCA REGISTRADA
HECHO EN CHICAGO, U.S.A.

SIGNET, SIGNET CLASSICS, MENTOR, PLUME and MERIDIAN BOOKS
are published by The New American Library, Inc.,
1301 Avenue of the Americas, New York, New York 10019

First Signet Printing, April, 1979

1   2   3   4   5   6   7   8   9

PRINTED IN THE UNITED STATES OF AMERICA

DAWN

---·◆·---

April 3, 1882

Chapter 1

He was an old-young man of thirty-four years, and he was about to die.

He did not know this.

It was April 3, 1882. The world was in flux. The United States of America was straining at the seams, bursting with growth and progress; crouched on the doorstep of the twentieth century.

There was to be no place for him in this new world. He knew this, and it troubled him. His two worst enemies were gnawing at him—time and himself. He was a misfit. There were only three roads to the future. Death, imprisonment or ridicule. There is no place in the world for a tame desperado; a gunman without guns is a clown. Imprisonment? Better to be a hunted animal than a caged beast.

Death.

When the moment arrived for this young man named Jesse Woodson James, he seemed to accept it as inevitable, and he went without a struggle.

The single explosion of a Smith & Wesson .44 revolver echoes through a small frame house in St. Joseph, Missouri, and the sound waves—like the ripples from a stone dropped in a pond—reach out to touch many people.

April 3, 1882. St. Joseph, Missouri. The sun rose at 6:10 A.M. Temperature: 44 degrees. Barometer: 30.74. The wind was from the southeast. It was a Monday.

It had rained during the night, and he could hear the water dripping from the eaves.

The shades were tightly drawn over the windows of the bedroom, and it was dark. He could hear the busy chatter of the birds, and he knew that the sky would be streaked with light in the east.

He lay awake, listening in the dark, his hands folded across

3

his chest. The brass bed sagged in the center and he was pressed close to the soft warmth of his wife. He could feel and hear her steady breathing. He knew that she was not asleep.

The house groaned and creaked with a language of its own. Green lumber hastily cut and nailed was now shrinking, straining against the bits of metal which held it. I am impatient, it said painfully. There should be time for seasoning, it said. I will warp, it said. I must be free, it said. The studs and timbers crackled. He listened. Too soon, he thought, too soon. Am I like a tree, he asked himself, cut so young, and uncured, and nailed into shapes that hold me?

One of the children coughed and moaned, restless in sleep. He heard through the thin wall. What will become of my son? he asked himself, and made no answer. There was none.

His wife stirred next to him. He could sense her tension, and for a moment he was afraid she might speak. Poor Zee. He had no answers for her. Her measured breathing went on.

He was tired and the pain in his chest persisted. He moved his hand down and his fingers touched the slight indentations where the bullets had entered. He should have been dead that day. A charmed life, some said.

Charmed?

His mind was a kaleidoscope reflecting the past in colored confusion against the backs of his eyelids. Where had it all gone? How quickly things were changed. When you thought about it in a single gulp, it was like nothing. You had to take each part and examine it to realize the long line of events. And yet the beginnings seemed so hazy, so almost unbelievable. He felt old in body, but his mind was still young. At least as young as it had ever been.

A feeling of depression assailed him and tugged at the lines in his face. Too much had happened. It didn't used to be this way. There had always been danger, but he was used to that; and the danger then had been mingled with excitement. That was it. The excitement was gone, and only the danger was left. It was like a dull ache, and there was something dirty, something nasty about it.

"You awake, Jesse?" Her voice was soft and expectant.

"Zee," he said, "you gotta stop calling me Jesse. It's Tom Howard. How many times I gotta tell you?"

"I'm sorry." She shifted in the bed, turning until she faced him.

"You make that mistake at the wrong time and all hell is liable to bust loose."

"I'm sorry," she said. "I think of you as Jesse. It just comes out when we're alone."

He was silent, not wanting the conversation to go on. He knew how it would be. He couldn't blame her, but there was nothing he could do about it. She was right. He knew that. He should go away, take his family to California and start in fresh, but in his mind he knew that it was too late.

"Why are the Fords here?" she asked.

"They're my friends," he said.

"You're planning something, aren't you?"

"What do you mean?" he asked.

"You said you were going to stop," she said. "You said there wouldn't be any more robberies. Jesse, don't do it. Please don't do it. We can go away. We can—"

"On what?" he hissed, an edge to his voice. "Go away on what? You think we can just move to California on air?"

"You could get a job here. We could save. We could—"

"A job doing what? Cleaning stables? Zee, I don't know how to do anything. I can shoot and I can ride. That's all I've ever done." He was silent for a long moment. "We're broke, Zee, but I got a plan. Just one more job. It's an easy one. With the money, we'll pull out. We'll have enough for a small spread and some stock and—"

She wasn't listening. She turned away and the bed trembled with her silent crying.

He compressed his lips and stared at the ceiling. She didn't understand. She thought that you just said magic words and everything turned out like a storybook. No, that wasn't fair. She was too real for that. It was just that she'd been through too much. Too much running and hiding, too much fear. She wanted a home for her children.

The furniture in the small, square room began to take shape in the burgeoning dawn. The airless room was heavy with the sour smell of sleep. He shifted to his side. The bed springs groaned and the pain in his chest made him grimace. His eyes strayed to the holstered revolvers hanging from the bedstead, and the rifle leaning against the wall within his reach.

It was useless to attempt more sleep. He pulled the cover back and sat up, swinging his legs off the bed. He reached out to take his pants from a chair and pulled them on. He stood up, scratching, then he buckled the heavy gunbelt at his waist. He went to the window and pulled the shade aside to look out. The sun was coming up. It was going to be a nice day.

In the back room of that small frame house on the hill overlooking St. Joseph, Missouri, Charley and Bob Ford were in bed.

Charley was snoring and the rasping sound annoyed Bob. He lay with his back to his brother and looked through the window at the growing light.

It had been a hellish night and he had not slept much. He was tired and irritated and he was afraid.

You could never tell with that man. You looked at him and he didn't seem any different than anyone else, but there was always the feeling that he knew everything that was going on. You had the feeling he was reading your mind. He was so damned quiet. And those eyes. They seemed to go right through you. Why the hell don't Charley stop that damn snoring? Yessir, that Jesse is a cold one. Is he really as fast as they say he is? I sure don't wanta find out. We gotta get him, though, we sure as hell gotta get him.

Turning, Bob reached out and grasped his brother's shoulder. He shook him hard. "Wake up!" he whispered.

"Uh? Wha'?"

"Wake up, Charley."

Sitting up, Charley Ford shook his head. He scratched his tousled head and rubbed the back of his neck. He blinked and peered at the window. "What time is it?"

"I don't know. It's morning," Bob said.

Charley glared at his younger brother. "What the hell you waking me up for?"

"We gotta talk."

"About what? I want some sleep, boy. We got a lot of riding to do tonight."

"That's what we gotta talk about. Tonight."

"Can't it wait?"

"No, it can't," Bob said. He spoke in tense, hushed tones. "I think he's suspicious. He knows something is up."

Charley was suddenly alert and there was the flicker of fear in his eyes. "What makes you say that?"

"I don't know. I just feel it. The way he looks at us. I just feel that he knows."

"You're just getting nervous," Charley said.

"Who wouldn't be?" Bob said.

"Calm down. How could he know anything? This bank job is his idea. He's the one asked us to join in."

"He's got friends," Bob said. "Suppose somebody saw me in Kansas City. Maybe Captain Craig told somebody. Maybe somebody already told him."

"And maybe you're crazy," Charley said. "If anybody told him you'd be a dead man now. Let me get some sleep."

"Charley. What if he finds out about Wood Hite?"

"He ain't gonna have time," Charley said. "Tonight he's gonna be dead."

"But he asked me about Dick Liddil. Why'd he do that? I tell you he knows Dick and me killed Wood Hite."

"Will you stop it. If he even thought you killed his cousin he'd blow your head off. He doesn't know anything." Charley dropped back, grumbling. He bunched the straw pillow under his head and tried to recapture his sleep.

Bob worried his lower lip with his teeth. He was in the clutch of a nagging fear. He was not a coward. It was simply that too much time had transpired since he had first agreed to kill Jesse James. He was a young man of twenty-one years and he had elected to extinguish a legend. He had spent the past four months awaiting an opportunity to throw down on the man, and in all that time he had not had a single chance. The watching and waiting had worn on his nerves, and he realized the wariness of his quarry.

Tonight was the night. The three of them were scheduled to ride north to Platte City to rob the bank there the next day. He had already informed Sheriff Jim Timberlake, and an ambush had been arranged.

If everything went right, Jesse James would be arrested or dead by tomorrow morning; and the Ford brothers would be ten thousand dollars richer.

It helped to think about the money, but not quite enough. He still had to get through the day, and it was like being caged with an animal. Jesse had been living by his gun for nineteen years, since the day he joined Quantrill. The Union Army couldn't take him, neither could the Pinkertons and a mess of sheriffs. A lot of ambushes had failed. If this one failed . . .

Bob Ford shuddered and the nerves made his legs jump.

Frank James awoke coughing. It was the racking, painful cough of the consumptive. He sat up and clutched both hands to his chest to ease the pain. He leaned over the bed and spit blood-flecked mucus into a bucket on the floor. The coughing ceased, but it left him fully awake and gasping for breath.

Two windows were wide open and it was cold in the room. This was part of the newfangled cure. Fresh air.

Sliding from under the covers, Frank dropped to the floor. He stood a moment in his long johns, scratching and yawning, then he took a mackinaw from a chair and pulled it over his arms. He did the buttons as he walked to the window.

The sun was climbing the mountains in the west. This Pecos River country was certainly a far cry from Missouri. It was a big lonely land, but that was why they had bought the ranch. It was the perfect hideout, although Jesse would never call it that. Rest Ranch Jesse called it. Frank smiled at the thought of it. You could never get Jesse to admit that he was running away from anything, even though they used to get over the Red River hell-bent, and beat it up here like tail-tucked curs. Taking a breather, Jesse called it.

Hiding out, I call it, Frank said to himself. He was a tall, slope-shouldered man with a large, tousled head. He was mild-mannered and his expression was almost benign.

Turning from the window, Frank paced the room. This was his third month at the ranch, and he was getting restless. It was a strange, ambiguous feeling. He was tired of the running, and he had the intelligence to know that time and progress were overtaking his kind. He wanted to put his guns down and stop looking over his shoulder for bounty hunters. It was always with a feeling of relief that he came off the Staked Plains and slipped into the valley that hid the ranch. Annie loved it here, and it was a good place for little Bobby. But it was the wrong kind of freedom. It was a self-chosen prison.

Frank stamped back to the bed. He piled the pillows and lit the lamp at the bed table for better light. He slid his legs under the covers and leaned back against the pillows, taking a leather-bound copy of Shakespeare's sonnets in his hand.

It was damned foolishness, he told himself. There are thousands of men who live on a ranch all their lives and never leave. I'm safe down here in Texas and I could make this place pay. He shook his head, knowing that he would never convince himself of this. There would always be a bounty hunter. He turned and gazed at the revolver on the table, the hammer dangerously cocked. It would always be like that.

Something has got to be done, he thought. I have to talk to Jesse. If we had a fair trial we could beat most of the charges against us. Any jury in Missouri would side with us against them damn railroads. Of course, that Northfield thing ain't gonna help. Killing that man was bad. No, I don't guess Jesse would go along with surrendering ourselves; and I sure couldn't do it unless it was okay with him. But dammit, what's gonna happen when we're too old to shoot and ride? That's the day we die. I'll have a talk with Jesse. I can't take much more of this life.

He heard the sounds of Annie in the kitchen, starting the wood stove. He would sure be glad when the chest thing cleared up and they could go back to sharing the same room.

She cursed the blue-bellies every morning, and this morning was no different. She was hard, frontier stock and just because Jeff Davis and that bunch of Virginia dandies had given in didn't mean that she had to kowtow to any damn Yankee.

Standing in her kitchen, working the grate of the stove with her left hand because a Yankee bomb had removed her right hand, she went slowly through her repertoire of curses. What her mutterings lacked in vulgarity they made up for in intensity. She blasted the North in general, then narrowed her attention to the blue-belly neighbors around her farm near Kearney, Missouri. She spent some time on Governor Crittenden, worked the railroads over, wished the Pinkertons into purgatory, and went down the line taking in anyone she could remember who had voiced an opinion against her boys.

She chunked wood into the stove and lit the fire, sliding the iron plate over the flames.

The corners of her mouth were pulled down in permament lines, and the crow's-feet at the corners of her deep-set eyes were etched in the leathery skin. At fifty-seven, she was an old woman; an embittered woman with a whip-lash tongue and a fierce loyalty to the dead Confederacy and her sons, Frank and Jesse.

Walking to a window, Zerelda Samuel gazed out beyond the barn to the fields. The morning light was spreading and the night damp glistened. Right now her boys ought to be out

there turning those fields with a plow. And where were they?
Frank down there in Texas and Jesse hiding in St. Joseph. To
make matters worse, young John was upstairs in bed recovering from a bullet wound received in a dance-hall fight.

She put the water to boil on the stove, then she dried her
hands on her apron and sat down at the kitchen table. It was
just two weeks since Jesse had visited. He had mentioned that
he was planning something with the Ford boys. This worried
her, and she told him that there was something about the
Fords that she didn't like. Jesse had laughed, but she wasn't
satisfied. If only she could put her finger on what was wrong.
There was one thing and maybe it was foolish. That young
Bob could look you straight in the eye and never waver. That
was something that took practice. To her way of thinking,
you couldn't trust a man who looked you straight in the eye.

She sighed deeply, shaking her head. Probably just an old
woman's foolishness, she thought. But the doubt persisted.

Before the sun went down, her fear would be substantiated,
and there would be a new name for her morning ritual.

On April 3, 1882, stocks opened lower; Richmond & Dan-
ville was 10 per cent lower, marking 130. Money was loaning
at 6 per cent on call. The morning newspapers reported that
the canals of Venice were to be filled and converted to
streets. A bleary-eyed Patrick McGinty was taken from his
cell in the Camden, New Jersey, jail, fined $3.85 for being
drunk and disorderly, and sent home. Nettie E. Penrod, aged
three months, strangled in her sleep, a victim of diphtheria.
The body of Peter Pickle was found suspended from a rope
at 160 Monroe Street, New York City. The Imperial Bank of
Germany reduced the rate of discount to 4.5 per cent.
Charles Fry, convicted of barn burning, was removed from
the Georgetown, Ohio, jail and hanged by persons unknown.
A mermaid was on exhibit at Taylor Hall in Trenton, New
Jersey. At exactly 6:30 A.M., President Arthur signed his veto
of the Chinese Bill. At 6:34 A.M., John Dooley of Arch
Street, Philadelphia, was killed by eastbound train No. 40 on
the Pennsylvania Railroad. He was fifty-five. At dawn, a
band of Tonto Apaches attacked a small ranch in the
Chiequita Mountains of Colorado, killing the wife and daughter of Thomas Mathison. In London, a gentleman named
Damala called at the residence of Miss Sarah Bernhardt. An
hour later they were quietly married at St. Andrews Church.

It was a typical beginning of another spring day. Millions of people stirred and rose from warm beds. Tragedy greeted some, joy awaited others. One event would rise above the others and withstand the obliteration of time. That drama was building in Missouri.

Martha Bolton dropped a plate and it shattered on the floor of the farmhouse just outside Richmond, Missouri. Martha ordered her fourteen-year-old daughter to clean up the mess, and went back to preparing breakfast, idly stirring the pot of grits.

From the minute she had answered the back door and looked upon the heavy figure with the full, black beard and the glowering eyes, she had been in a nervous state. That was almost two weeks ago. Jesse James had come in the night and Bob had gone away with him. Each day the nervousness had gotten worse.

She was plagued with doubts. It was Martha who had visited Governor T. T. Crittenden at the St. James Hotel in Kansas City and made the arrangements for her brothers, Charley and Bob Ford, to receive amnesty from the law in return for killing Jesse James. It wasn't only the reward money that interested Martha—though the money would certainly come in handy—but there was also the matter of Wood Hite.

Leaving the stove, she went to the window that looked out over the rear yard. At the edge of the field she could see the pile of stones. Wood Hite's body was under those stones. It made her break into a nervous sweat every time she thought about it. He had been killed in her house, and Bob had triggered the gun. Dick Liddil had been present and if Jesse ever got his hands on Dick and made him talk . . . Wood Hite was Jesse's favorite cousin and he was asking an awful lot of questions about his disappearance. That was why Martha had made the arrangements with Crittenden.

It seemed easy enough at the time, what with Bob and Charley being just like lawmen, and having the state behind them. But now she just didn't know. Could you trust the state? Did Jesse know about the plot, and was Bob already dead? She hadn't heard from the boys and she was frightened.

Cole Younger did not want Jesse James to die. He wanted something far worse for him. He wanted him to go through the rest of his natural life in the deadening ritual of prison.

He had been awake long before the guards began their morning rounds, staring at his blank walls in the small cell at the Minnesota State Prison at Stillwater. He had been sentenced to life for his part in the Northfield holdup, and for nearly six years now he had lived within the confines of this cell.

Jim Younger had been badly wounded at Northfield and Cole could never forget that Jesse had insisted they shoot Jim to hasten the escape, and when Cole refused, Jesse and Frank left them. Cole's hatred had grown.

On that morning, as he did every morning, Cole prayed to whatever gods were left to him that Jesse James would occupy the adjoining cell. He relished the thought.

The metal-gray sky was streaked with blossoms of yellow sun. The morning air was chilled, but it would warm as the day progressed.

Helen Heywood did not see the beauty of the day. To her it was just one more day that those murderers would be free to draw breath.

The city of Northfield had all but forgotten the robbery. Six years had passed and too much was happening. The City Council was more concerned about putting the new electric lights on the main street. But Helen did not forget.

Childless and alone in the small frame house, she waited for her morning newspaper. When it came she would scan it carefully for news about the James boys. She had been doing this for years without results. At first it had been frustrating, but now it was a habit.

One of them had shot her Joseph to death at the Northfield Bank. It did not interest her that others had died at Northfield on that day. Joseph Lee Heywood had been murdered.

She was a silent, patient avenger.

Captain Henry Craig was not ordinarily an early riser and for this reason he was surly and annoyed by Jim Timberlake's brisk manner.

Consulting his watch, Craig winced and frowned. He reached out and dropped a spoonful of sugar into his coffee and stirred it moodily. He was also annoyed that he was in

Timberlake's room at the St. James Hotel. After all, he was Police Commissioner of Kansas City and Timberlake was just a sheriff. But Timberlake had the governor's ear, and Craig had to admit that his plan was good.

A third annoying factor was that Timberlake had just consumed a huge breakfast, something Craig's ulcer would not allow, and he was now on his third cup of coffee.

"You're sure you can trust these Fords?" Craig asked.

"Course you can't trust 'em," Timberlake said.

"Then maybe this whole thing is a wild-goose chase. I don't like working with their kind."

"Then why bother posting rewards?" Timberlake said. "You put a price on a man's life, it's the same as painting a target on his back. And you're dangling that reward to bring a certain type out of the crowd. There's only two things will make a Judas. Greed and fear. In this case we got a little of both. I been watching the Ford boys for a long time. I happen to know they killed Wood Hite and they know that I know it. Only a bigger fear will stop them from going through with this."

Craig was not interested in Timberlake's philosophy. He was basically a politician and his interest in the capture of the James brothers was largely political. It was the only reason he was here in a hotel room at this time of morning. He didn't want to miss taking the credit for masterminding the capture.

"You're ready to go as soon as we get word from the governor?" Craig asked.

"Yes," Timberlake said. "The train is all set. Two freight cars and a caboose."

"Freight cars?"

"Yes. I didn't want anyone wondering what a special was doing going north. This way it will be just another freight. The Jameses have too many friends. But there shouldn't be any hitch about this. We'll have the men in one car, horses in another. We unload below Platte City and ride south to intersect the road."

"It sounds all right."

"If the breaks are with us," Timberlake said.

"They'd better be," Craig said.

Two men waiting for the signal that would put the gears into motion, setting up the ambush for Jesse James. They had both worked for many months for this day, and it was Timberlake who had first approached Martha Bolton.

The hem of the long dressing robe snapping about his ankles, Governor T. T. Crittenden swept along the main hall of the governor's mansion at Jefferson City. Without pausing, he pushed through the heavy doors and marched into his study where his secretary and the messenger were waiting.

He took the proffered envelope and went to his desk. He dropped into the heavy leather chair and tore the envelope open, extracting the paper within. He tugged at his muttonchop whiskers as he read, pursing his lips.

"Good, good," he said finally. He looked up at the secretary. "Take this message for Captain Craig in Kansas City," he said. "'Your plan has my heartiest support. Proceed according to your outline. May this bring an end to the matter. Good luck.'" He turned to the messenger. "See that the message is sent without delay."

"Yes, sir."

Crittenden rose from the chair and left the room. It was too early for breakfast. He went to his bedroom and slipped back into bed.

If it wasn't one thing, it was another. It had taken a long time for Missouri to stamp out the night riders, and now they would be rid of the Jameses. If the people of the state only knew what this meant for business, they wouldn't be helping those damned outlaws. In the East it was believed that Missouri was a lawless frontier, and businessmen refused to invest money under such conditions. He didn't enjoy the idea of employing brigands like the Fords, but if it would result in the capture of Jesse James, so be it.

Many threads, each separate, but all woven by circumstance into a giant web. And the weaver was a nonentity, a thing called Hate.

It was not the hate of any one person for another, nor was it a hatred of weeks or months. It was a hatred that had spread a long time across a vast land, a rolling tumultuous emotion that engulfed towns and counties, drawing men into sharply divided armed camps. North or South. Black or White. Missouri or Kansas.

In two hours a bearded outlaw living under the assumed

name of Thomas Howard would be shot to death. A man
would die and a legend would be born.

A legend born of hatred in a cornfield near Kearney, Missouri, in the spring of 1863.

THE
BEGINNING

---◄●►---

1850-1863

Chapter 2

The roots of this narrative are imbedded in Logan County, Kentucky, where John James married Mary Poor in 1807. Their progeny numbered three daughters and five sons, Robert Sallee James being born in 1818.

It was this Robert who studied theology at Georgetown (Kentucky) College. While a student there he fell in love with a girl named Zerelda Cole, a Scott County child who had attended a Catholic convent in Lexington. Zerelda Cole's father was dead, but she could not get along with her stepfather, Robert Thomason, so she remained with her Uncle James M. Lindsay when her mother and stepfather moved to Clay County, Missouri. Both parents of Rev. Robert S. James were dead at the time of his marriage to Zerelda Cole on December 28, 1841. The Rev. Y. R. Pitts officiated.

The newlyweds took their meager belongings and an inbred devotion to the South, and moved west, settling in Clay County, Missouri, where the farmland was proven and the neighbors were Southerners.

Their first child, Alexander Franklin, was born on January 10, 1844. They called him Frank. A second son, Robert, was born on July 19, 1845, but he died in infancy. Zerelda's grief over his death caused her to bear a certain resentment toward her third son, Jesse Woodson, who was born September 5, 1847. It was some time before she could reconcile herself to this replacement of the mourned baby.

The only daughter of this marriage was Susan L. James, born on November 25, 1849.

Preacher James was never a success at tilling the soil, and although he founded several small churches in Clay County, this would not feed a growing family. On April 12, 1851, he set out for the California gold fields to make his fortune. He arrived on the Pacific Coast on August 1, 1851, and eighteen days later he died of fever and was buried in an unmarked grave in Hangtown.

Twenty-six-year-old Zerelda was left alone on the farm with her three children. She faced bitter years, but she dug in with the tenacity that was to be a part of her all her life, and scratched a meager living from the soil. To work a portion of the farm she borrowed the slaves of a friendly neighbor, Benjamin Simms. Frank was seven and Jesse was four years old.

The Kansas-Missouri border was rumbling with violence. On the surface it was pro-slavery Missouri opposed by abolitionist Kansas, but there were deeper motives bringing the Kansas night riders to burn and pillage in Missouri. In the Western migration, farmland—not adventure—was the impetus. Each new group moved only so far as was necessary to find vacant land. Missouri was already beginning to prosper when the emigrants sank their plows into Kansas soil. For some reason Missouri always maintained an economic edge over her neighbor, and there was considerable envy and malice involved when a Kansan put a torch to a Missouri farm. There were retaliations and counter-retaliations. Eight years before the soldiers of the Confederacy fired on Fort Sumter, there was vicious fighting on the Kansas-Missouri border.

Frank and Jesse James stepped from their cradles into a life of terror, vengeance and sudden death. No man dared answer his door with a light at his back. No man approached a house without warning. "Kill or be killed" was as basic as the three R's. The James boys teethed on the butt of an old Walker Colt, and two things were taught to them as fact: night would follow day; Kansans and Yankees deserved killing.

On September 30, 1852, Zerelda married her neighbor and friend, Benjamin Simms, but there was a clash of personalities in this match. Simms demanded that Zerelda transfer her property to his name. She refused and they were separated. Before divorce proceedings could be started, Simms was thrown from a horse and killed. Zerelda told inquisitive persons the reason she and Simms failed to get along was because of his unfriendly attitude toward Frank and Jesse. She went back to using the name of James. On September 26, 1855, she married Dr. Reuben Samuel, who was twenty-seven years old, and a native of Kentucky. This marriage was a success, for Zerelda found it easy to dominate the mild-mannered Samuel. They had four children: Sarah L., born December 26, 1858; John, born May 25, 1861; Fannie Quantrill, born October 18, 1863; and Archie Peyton, born July 26, 1866.

Frank James was now eleven and Jesse was eight. Frank was a tall, gangling boy with a long face. He was quiet and studious, and the favorite of easygoing Reuben Samuel. Jesse was shorter in stature, and he had a stubborn, rebellious streak. Modern psychologists would categorize him quickly. His father had "deserted" him when he was four. His first stepfather had disliked him. The mother he worshipped showed a marked preference for his older brother, referred to him always as "Mister Frank." The second stepfather, of whom he was fond, was also partial toward Frank. Jesse had deep-set feelings of rejection, and he spent his childhood compensating for this by being wilder than his brother, and proving a superiority as a marksman and a rider. Like most "born" leaders, he was driven by a sense of inferiority.

In the latter half of the 1850s, the Kansas raiders became organized into bands called Jayhawkers and Red Legs, and they set the border aflame under the hand of General Jim Lane. The Missouri fighters needed a leader. He came to them, a fugitive from Kansas, a wild-eyed psychopath with Napoleonic delusions—William Clarke Quantrill.

Missourians were ready to follow anyone who would lead them against Kansas, and Quantrill's intense hatred for the Jayhawkers appealed to them. Several small groups of bushwhackers, as the Missouri raiders were known, banded together under Quantrill's black flag, and they exacted a terrible vengeance against the Kansas raiders.

The nation was plunged into civil war in 1861. Missouri was officially in the Union and a state militia was organized, mostly in the northern portion of the state. The men who rode with Quantrill followed their hearts and became members of the outlawed Confederate Partisan Rangers. Yankee troops in Missouri were treated like occupation forces, and Quantrill was heralded as a sainted hero.

Frank James was seventeen, and despite heavy leanings toward Quantrill, he rode south and joined the Confederate force under General Benjamin McCulloch. His service was short-lived. After the Battle of Wilson's Creek, he was captured by a Union patrol. As was the custom in the early days of the war, he was given a field parole, meaning that he swore never again to bear arms against the United States Government.

Back in Clay County, the battlefield promise rankled the proud and sensitive Frank James. He was ashamed of having surrendered to the blue-bellied Federals, and he spent his time bragging about how the Confederates had whipped the pants off the damned Yankees at Wilson's Creek.

In Liberty, Missouri, Frank flourished a pistol during a drinking bout, and threatened to kill any Union soldier who dared molest him. An entire squad dared and Frank found himself in the Liberty jail.

Zerelda used her influence with Silas Woodson, prominent Missouri politician and governor-to-be, and Frank was released.

Unable to reconcile himself to the additional shame of being jailed after his show of braggadocio, Frank violated his parole and joined Quantrill's guerrillas. He became a hunted man, and he drew his entire family into the circle of suspicion. The Samuel farm was now a refuge and meeting place for the Missouri raiders. Federal soldiers made frequent visits, trying to learn the whereabouts of Frank and Quantrill.

In the shadow of Frank's reputation, young Jesse was branded an outlaw before he lifted a gun in anger. The Federal soldiers could not find Quantrill's elusive raiders, so they contented themselves with harassing their families.

Dr. Samuel did his best to keep Jesse neutral, but it was to be only a matter of time before something triggered the emotions of hatred that were boiling within him.

The pattern of his life was being drawn, events were piling up that would channel him into the mainstream of his particular life. It was as though the foundation were being carefully laid to support a life of violence. It was not a decision, it was an emotional upheaval.

Chapter 3

It was the plowing season, spring, 1863.

General Joe Hooker's Union Army had been slaughtered at Chancellorsville. Stonewall Jackson had been killed. The butternut and gray was surging over the Mason-Dixon Line like a wave of locusts. The general opinion in the land was that the Union was a lost cause. General Lee was massing his army for a push into Pennsylvania and a place called Gettysburg.

In Missouri the news of continued Federal losses made Quantrill step up his raids. He fought in open combat with the Union patrols, generally winning. The Union Army on the other hand was frightened. They appeased this fear by intensifying their brutal treatment of noncombatants.

A blue-uniformed patrol rode up the long, rutted lane and reined in before the front porch of the Samuel farmhouse. Mrs. Samuel and her daughter Susan were on the porch. The older woman was coldly antagonistic.

"We're looking for Frank James," the sergeant said, grinning.

"He ain't here," Zerelda said.

"Didn't 'spect he would be. But I reckon you folks can tell us where he is."

"We haven't heard from him."

The sergeant chuckled. "You Rebs are sure the damndest liars I ever seen," he said. "Where's the doctor and that other kid of yourn?"

"They're in the fields," Zerelda said.

"We better have a talk with them." He wheeled his horse and cantered over the soft lawn, the squad following. They paused at the barn, then seeing the two figures at the crawling plow, they rode down into the field.

Jesse and his stepfather stopped their work and turned to face the approaching cavalry. This had happened many times before and they regarded the smiling sergeant with sullen expressions.

"We're looking for Frank," the soldier said.

"He's not here," Samuel said.

"I reckon I can see that, but we figured you'd be happy to tell us where he is."

"We have no idea," Samuel said.

"Well, now, Mr. Samuel, I think maybe you're lying. But then, maybe it's just that your memory is bad. We figure on helping you remember." He nodded at one of his men. "Take him!"

A rope snaked out and the loop fell over Dr. Samuel's shoulders. The slack was taken up. The soldier spurred his horse, and Dr. Samuel was dragged, running, toward the barn.

A cry of rage broke from Jesse's throat. He dropped the leads to the mule and ran after his stepfather. Two horsemen went after him and boxed him in, herding him with the points of their bayonets.

Dr. Samuel was dragged to the barn. One end of the rope was flung over a beam and the noose was fixed to Dr. Samuel's neck. Jesse was tied to a post.

"Now then, Samuel," the sergeant said, "you're gonna tell us where to find Frank James or you're gonna hang." There was no answer. "Pull him up a little to show him how it feels," the sergeant said.

The soldier nudged his horse forward and Dr. Samuel was lifted from his feet. He spun free, his hands clutching at the rope in his throat, his face reddening. They lowered him to the ground.

"That's just a little sample," the sergeant said. "It can be a lot worse. You gonna talk?"

"Leave 'im alone!" Jesse screamed, straining at his ropes. "He don't know nothin'!"

"But maybe you do, eh?" the sergeant said, turning to the youngster.

"Maybe I do!" Jesse shouted. "But I'll never tell you, you blue-belly sonofabitch!"

The sergeant's arm shot out and he lashed a quirt across Jesse's face. "Work him over!" he shouted. "Make the stinkin' little Reb whimper."

Two soldiers stepped forward with short lengths of rope.

They tore Jesse's shirt away and administered a severe beating. The boy suffered in silence.

They went back to Dr. Samuel and pulled him up until he passed out. They revived him and repeated the maneuver several times.

Realizing they were going to get no information by torture, they left, the doctor being cut down by the family and revived and they took Jesse with them, charging him with aiding the enemy. He was locked in the Liberty jail.

Through a lack of evidence and the efforts of Silas Woodson, Jesse was released. He returned to the farm and the spring plowing. The following week a squad of Union soldiers arrived at the Samuel farm. This time they arrested Zerelda and Susan, who was in her early teens, taking them to the jail at St. Joseph.

It was common knowledge that the Jameses possessed fierce family loyalties, and the Federals expected Frank and the guerrillas to stage a raid on the jail to release his mother and sister. The jail was an unsanitary hovel. A month passed and the raid did not come off. When Susan contracted pneumonia, and was near death, the two were released. They returned to the farm and Susan was nursed back to health.

The efforts of the Union soldiers had failed to extract any information, but they had succeeded in creating a demon. Jesse took his musket and revolver and left to join Quantrill. He was a slight youth of fifteen, but he possessed a towering rage. He did not ride away to fight for the Confederacy. His motive was the epitome of simplicity—to kill as many Union soldiers as was humanly possible.

He went directly to Frank and the older brother took him to Quantrill.

"He's too young," Quantrill said.

Frank argued, but Quantrill was firm. He insisted that Jesse return home, but Jesse flatly refused.

It was a deadlock until Bloody Bill Anderson and Cole Younger, two of Quantrill's chief lieutenants, took the boy's side.

"He can ride with me," Anderson said. "I'll look after him."

Frank was also a member of Anderson's command, and Jesse kept to his brother's side. Within a month it was apparent that Quantrill had been wrong. Jesse fought with a fury that even the guerrillas had to admit was inhuman.

"That boy," Anderson said, "is the best fighter in the group. He's not afraid of the devil himself."

There was nothing Jesse would not do if it resulted in the death of Yankee troops. With his youthful, delicate features, he could assume the disguise of a young girl and act as a lure for Federal officers. In this guise he paid a visit to a bawdy-house in Independence, Missouri, and discovered that Federal officers were frequent visitors there. The following night he led an ambush near the hospitable house, trapped twelve officers and killed them all.

His reputation was growing steadily.

Chapter 4

Jesse's first big fight was at Richfield, in Clay County, Missouri; twelve guerrillas against the Federal garrison. This was followed by two years of slaughter, danger, hell-for-leather riding and shooting. It was a bitter, bloody education for a young man.

Official reports and letters sketch the trail that Jesse was riding.

The first was a report on Richfield from Captain Joseph Schmitz of the Twenty-fifth Missouri Infantry to Colonel Chester Harding, Jr.:

U.S. ARSENAL, CLAY COUNTY, MO.
May 22, 1863

SIR:

I received your letter of instruction, duly, from Richmond, Mo., of the 16th instant, in regard to the scouring out of Fishing River Bottom. I accordingly made every disposition of the forces under my command to secure success in the matter, but, unluckily, as you are already aware, the movement commenced about one hour and a half too late. The following special programme was laid down to be pursued: Lieutenant [George W.] Shinn, with his command, was to leave Camden at 9 P.M. on Tuesday, the 19th instant; Lieutenant Fleming, of the Provisional Missouri Militia, was to join Lieutenant [Louis] Grafenstein at Richfield, Mo., before 9 o'clock on Tuesday evening at which hour they were to start to their different destinations; Lieutenant Fleming to the mouth of the Fishing River, where he was to meet Lieutenant Shinn, with whom he wants to act in concert in scouring the country on each side of the river up to the lower bridge. Lieutenant Grafenstein, whom I had previ-

ously stationed at Richfield, with 16 men, and who were
not mounted, were to start at the same time to the lower
bridge, where they were directed to lie hidden and guard
the roads on both sides of the river.

In accordance with this arrangement, Lieutenant Fleming left here at 6 P.M. for Richfield. When arriving
near that place, he met two messengers with the intelligence of the bloody work; and shortly after, while hurry-
ing up his men, he met Sergeant Clymo and the balance
of Lieutenant Grafenstein's command (13 men) on the
retreat to this post, having been assured by citizens of
the place that the bushwhackers numbered from 60 to
100. . . . The whole command [being] but 36, all told,
they concluded it best to return to this place (particularly because the reported force to oppose was too large
to attack in the night without knowing definitely the situation of the affairs in the place), which they did immediately. After making every preparation possible for an
early pursuit next morning, we anxiously awaited daylight.

At dawn, Captains Garth and Tracey, of the Provisional Reserve Missouri Militia, with 40 men from
Liberty, were here and ready to start in pursuit. With
them I sent Lieutenant [H. C.] Carlile and (Dr. [J. Q.]
Egelston volunteering) with 35 men. I concluded to give
our party under Dr. Egelston's supervision. After nearly
reaching Richfield, they first learned the true conditions
of affairs, and the sad result of the decoy and ambush of
Lieutenant Grafenstein and Captain Sessions and squad.

The facts are simply as follows, to wit: Sixteen bushwhackers made their appearance 2 miles east of the
town of Richfield, in the afternoon of Tuesday; two of
them went to a house in the neighborhood, acting as if
drunk, swearing they were Quantrill's men, etc. The men
at whose house they were started immediately after they
left and reported to Lieutenant Grafenstein, as above,
when Lieutenant Grafenstein and Captain Sessions and
3 men started out to look into the matter. After getting
out of the place 1½ miles, they were fired upon from the
thick brush. Captain Sessions and Private Rapp fell the
first fire; Lieutenant Grafenstein was hit soon after, and
had to stop; the three were then rushed upon by the

party of murderers. Rapp was robbed and left for dead.
Captain Sessions was shot again two or three times
through the head, and Lieutenant Grafenstein, after surrendering himself a prisoner, was coolly shot twice
through the head also (a woman at the same time, near
by, begging for his life). They both were stripped and
plundered also. The gang then pursued the two remaining number of the squad in a direction not directly
toward Richfield, but reached that place in about twenty
minutes after the first firing, the two boys beating them
in and escaping from them. In the meantime, someone
passing near where Rapp was brought him in to town,
and was having his wounds dressed. After the devils entering the town, and learning that Rapp was not killed,
one of them went directly to him and shot him three
times more, and left him for dead the second time. (He
yet will probably recover.) They then commenced to
pillage the Union citizens particularly, but really made
but little distinction between the loyal and disloyal; and
after doing this pretty effectually, and destroying the
Union flag, cutting the pole, etc., they left the place, on
the same road they entered, about 9 or 10 o'clock the
same night. . . .

The citizens around that country are all sympathizers,
with very few exceptions, and it is hard to get information from them. . . .

From the best information that I can obtain, there
were but 16 or 18 men of the bushwhackers, and
were under command of one Ferdinand Scott, who was
recognized by persons who know him well; so also were
the following named: Frank Turner, L. Easton, Frank
James, Louis Vandever, Louis Gregg, and Churchill, and
Moses McCoy, the husband of Mrs. McCoy, now on parole at your place. Joe Hart was not with the gang at
Richfield on Tuesday evening, but was reported to have
met them at the place before mentioned, 12 miles north
of Liberty, on Wednesday (by the men at the house they
stopped). Hart said then that he came from St. Joe
(direct) and visited Mrs. McCoy.

On July 15, 1863, Sam Breitenbaugh at Lexington, Missouri, reported to Brigadier General Ewing as follows:

I left Kansas City yesterday morning on the Ogden.
Arrived here at 5 o'clock the same day, and the first
news I learned was the murder of 4 Union men and 1
girl, and 9 wounded, by the bushwhackers, numbering
40. This sad affair took place in Freedom Township, in
the German settlement, some 15 miles from this city.
After they executed their hellish purposes, they went in
the direction of the Mound, about 9 miles from town,
and dispersed in small bands of from 5 to 10, some going toward the Sni, and in various directions. This band
is headed by one W. T. Anderson [Bloody Bill] who
formerly lived in this place. They captured 1 of the militiamen, and paroled him to report to Colonel McFer-
ran, and to no other, to be exchanged for one notorious
William Ogden, said to be at this time a prisoner in
Kansas. Failing to comply, his life is to be the forfeit.
Colonel Childs was taken by them and led to the brush,
there to be hanged. Through the intercession of former
friends, his life was spared, on conditions. Those conditions the colonel was not at liberty to confide to your
correspondent. The noted bushwhacker Dave Pool had
been Colonel Childs' prisoner. This Pool has declared
that he intended killing 50 Union men, in retaliation for
the killing of Colonel Parker, etc. On my way up to
your city, we passed about 15 or 20 bushwhackers, on a
point of timber land, a few miles above Sibley (bottom
land), about 7 A.M. They appeared to be preparing their
breakfast. The boat was not within range. Had she been,
no doubt we would have received a volley from their
firearms.

In continued explanation of the situation at that time, here
is quoted a special dispatch to the Missouri *Democrat:*

LEAVENWORTH, August 26, 1863

General Lane has returned to Lawrence. A meeting
was held on his return. Lane said the citizens had killed
41 of Quantrill's men. Majors Clark and Plumb were
denounced. The people of Baldwin disputed Quantrill in
passing a ford, and say if Plumb had done his duty they
could have whipped the rebels. Lane is organizing forces,

and says he will go into Missouri on the 9th of September. He left General Ewing only on a pledge that Ewing would issue an order directing all the citizens of Jackson, Cass, Bates, and part of Vernon Counties, except those in Kansas City, Westport, Harrisonville, and Independence, to leave the county within fifteen days. Ewing had issued the order, and the people of Kansas are going into Missouri to see the order executed. . . . Ewing is frightened, and in the chase after Quantrill was in a complete quandary. He is looked upon as being a general without heart or brains. . . .

Quantrill had with him Sam Hays, brother of Up. [Upton] Hays, Dick Yeager, Holt, George Todd, and Younger [Cole], with 150 more of the citizens of Platte, Clay, La Fayette, Jackson, Cass, and Bates Counties, not over 300 in all. Quantrill's men are tonight reported scattered in Missouri.

Martial law is published in Leavenworth, but is practically null, as there is no provost-marshal or soldiers here to enforce it, and nothing to do if they were here. Martial law opened as a farce and ended in a fearful tragedy. One thousand Kansas men will be in Missouri this week.

Up to this morning 183 bodies were buried in Lawrence. The remains of 7 more bodies are found. One hundred and eighty-two buildings were burned; 80 of them were brick; 65 of them were on Massachusetts Street. There are 85 widows and 240 orphans made by Quantrill's raid. . . .

A man was today tried in Lawrence, and found guilty of being a spy for Quantrill, and was hung.

Here are two more documents that are of interest:

HEADQUARTERS
HARRISONVILL STATION, Mo.
October 24, 1863

LIEUT. H. HANNAHS,
ACTG. ASST. ADJT. GEN., DISTRICT OF THE BORDER:

LIEUTENANT: Yesterday morning while our messengers were returning from Pleasant Hill with the mail they were fired on by a party of bushwhackers. One of them was taken prisoner; the other escaped with the mail and got to station at 10 A.M. About 4 P.M. the one who was taken prisoner also came in, bringing a note from Lieutenant Wedington, of bushwhacking notoriety. The note I send you just as I received it. About 8 P.M. last night two men of Company M, Sixth Kansas Volunteers, came in and reported that they were taken prisoners by Wedington's band on the 20th. They are the men referred to in the note. They were permitted to bring their horses in with them. Two of Wedington's men escorted them to within 2 miles of this station, and then sent them in.

Very respectfully,

W. DOUDNA
Major, Commanding Station

Inclosure:

NEAR HARRISONVILLE, October 20, 1863
COLONEL CLARK,
COMMANDING NINTH KANSAS:

SIR: I this morning have captured two of your soldiers, and, in accordance with the custom heretofore, they would be executed, but I release them from two considerations: One is that they are boys, and again, whereas Colonel Quantrill, commanding the Confederate guerrillas, is absent, the command is given to me during his absence. I heartily regret the inhuman treatment of prisoners here on the border; but I, by this act, propose carrying it on in entirely a different way. I have released your men, and am willing to do it hereafter. Now, let us conduct the war in a way in which we will not be ashamed of in after years.

Yours, etc.,

WEDINGTON,
Lieutenant, Confederate Guerrillas

To show further the general climate of the situation at the time the guerrillas were operating, here is a report from Colonel C. Franklin, Provisional Army of the Confederate States of America, sent direct to President Jefferson Davis under date of November 6, 1863, from "Near Camp Bragg, Arkansas":

If truth needed an apology, I would apologize. Your earnest desire to preserve unimpaired the boundaries of the Confederate States is well known, and that you seek that, by striving to preserve in the council and in the field a morality which shall deserve success is equally well known. This fact alone emboldens me to call your attention to some most unpleasant truths.

When Jo. Shelby, or any of the old jayhawking captains, makes a raid into Missouri, he and all his followers adopt the pirates' law of property. Mankind are considered but objects of prey, and, astonishing and painful as the knowledge must be, they rob indiscriminately friend and foe. If such work is not soon arrested, it may be continued indefinitely, for not a friend will be left in all that country to be ruined. Shelby boasts that on the last raid he completely "gutted Boonville"; also that many Southern families, hearing of his approach, had removed their goods out of doors, expecting him to burn their houses. In fact, sir, the Shelby-Marmaduke raids in that country have transferred to the Confederate uniform all the dread and terror which used to attach to the Lincoln blue. The last horse is taken from the widow and orphan, whose husband and father has fallen in the country's service. No respect is shown to age, sex, or condition. Women are insulted and abused. On the other hand, General Steele, the Federal commander, is winning golden opinions by his forbearance, justice, and urbanity. I state this without amplifying. Anyone can judge what will follow. If I dare venture a suggestion, it would be that the men who have thus deported themselves should be removed from the district, for their very names have become omens of evil. . . . Yet these men have friends in high, very high places; that constitutes the difficulty. That is the only reason why I trouble you with it. . . . There are too many men implicated in these wrongs, too much whisky drank in high places, too much disorganization in this army corps for these things to be redressed here by the powers that be. . . .

My high regard for your character makes me think that whatever is right has your sanction; whatever is wrong has your condemnation. Then I conclude that, with an army of which you are the chief, private property must be respected, paid for, or some receipt given binding the Government. Also that the very name of woman must be sacred. . . .

Permit me to reiterate: I do not wish to trust either myself, or my men, or my cause to any drunken officer. I do not wish to belong to a mob, or an army which, by its conduct, cannot be distinguished from one. I will neither aid nor abet any man, or set of men, nor any army, that allows women either to be insulted or robbed.

Indorsement:

JANUARY 19, 1864

ADJUTANT-GENERAL:
For attention. For the particular case, it would be well to send a copy of the within to General E. Kirby Smith, that he may have due inquiry made, with a view to the suppression of such shameful outrages as are described.

JEFFERSON DAVIS

Jesse James almost lost his life when his band was attacked by a superior Union force on August 13, 1864, at the Flat Rock Ford over Grand River. Shot through the right lung, he was carried to the home of Captain John A. Rudd, in Carroll County. His friends—Gooly Robertson, Nat Tigue, Ole Shepherd, and Peyton Long—were determined to guard him with their lives if need be. They all expected the boy to die, and Jesse handed Peyton Long a plain gold ring, with instructions to give it to his beloved sister Susan.

But he was nursed back to health by Mrs. John Rudd and Mr. and Mrs. S. Neale, and was well enough to take part in the Battle of Centralia on September 27, 1864, when he singled out the commander, Major Johnson, and killed him. He saw a Spencer rifle ball pierce the neck of the gallant

George Todd on October 23, 1864, near Independence, Missouri. And he was present when Bloody Bill Anderson died on October 27 near Orrick in southwest Ray County, Missouri.

Chapter 5

Generals Sheridan and Ord sat their horses on the roadside below the town and waited. A bulky, round-shouldered officer in mud-spattered uniform rode up and reined in. His bearded face was stern. He nodded toward the town.

"Is General Lee up there?" he asked.

"I believe he is, sir," Sheridan said.

Grant nodded and sighed. "Well," he said, "let's get this over with."

They rode into Appomattox Court House, and the war was over. It was Palm Sunday.

In the West it took time for the news of the surrender to reach the scattered Union commands and the Rebel partisans, but by the middle of April, 1865, many Missouri farmers had returned to their plowing and the bitter realities of reconstruction.

A group of men, including Jesse James, rode toward the old brick school—now called the Burns School—on their way to Lexington, Missouri, to surrender their arms.

Provost Marshal Major Rodgers had not yet heard of their intention to surrender. Coming up the Salt Pond Road, seven miles from Lexington, with a detachment of Union cavalry, he saw the approaching guerrillas. Without asking questions, the Northerners opened fire.

Startled by the sudden attack, the guerrillas returned the fire, then scattered and ran. Jesse was shot in the right lung, the same lung that had been shattered during the war. But he kept his saddle and fled south on the Prairie Church Road. He was bleeding internally, but five Federals were in pursuit, and he kept on.

Adjacent to the A. A. Young farm, he left the road, jumping a fence. He turned northwest, galloping over the fields. Near the Young house he overtook Mrs. Young, who was carrying the water from the nearby spring.

"Madam," he asked, "have you seen any soldier this morning."

Mrs. Young said that she had not.

Jesse continued riding northwest, and from the open space near the house he saw his pursuers cautiously riding south on the road he had abandoned. Jesse spurred his horse, rode between the original Young house and a log kitchen some fifteen feet west, crossed the family garden plot, and about four hundred yards north came to a rail fence. Here, unable to make his horse jump the fence, he left the animal and continued on foot north through the timber to a drift coal mine on Garrison Creek.

The five Federal soldiers caught up with the horse, then turned east and north, returning to the Burns School, where the shooting had occurred an hour earlier.

Jesse remained in the drift mine until dark, then crept to the brick house of Dr. Barnett Lankford (now the Charles Estabrooks farm), where he was given food and treatment. After two days he was able to ride again. Provided with food, he went south through Johnson County to a place eight miles southeast of Clinton in Henry County, Missouri.

Here Jesse learned that his mother had been banished from Missouri for her outspoken Confederate sympathies, and was living in Rulo, Nebraska. His wound was treated by a Dr. A. B. Hereford, but he was certain that he was going to die, and he began the grueling trek to Nebraska to be with his mother.

A week after this shooting, Dave Pool and forty other guerrillas surrendered and told of how Jesse James had been wounded. Provost Marshal Rodgers did not even bother to list his name among those who surrendered, so sure was he that the young man had died. This omission made Jesse James a hunted man. John L. Jones, later of Cottonwood Falls, Kansas, was the private in the Third Wisconsin Cavalry who claimed the distinction of having fired the last shot of the Civil War in Missouri by wounding Jesse James.

In Nebraska, Jesse begged his mother to take him back to Missouri so that he could die on his native soil. More dead than alive, he was transported on a flatboat down the Missouri River and landed across from Kansas City. There he was taken to the Mimmbs home, where he was nursed back to health by his first cousin, Zerelda (Zee) Mimmbs, whom he later married.

THE
JAMES GANG

———— •◆• ————

1865-1876

Chapter 6

They straggled home. They walked, they rode gaunt, slat-sided horses. They came by river boat. They stole rides on cattle cars. They were the defeated. They carried strange names in their heads: Spotsylvania, Manassas, Shiloh, Cold Harbor, Antietam. They had left their homes to fight against the merchants and mechanics of the North, and they had lost.

To them the war was boredom and butchery. They were disillusioned and bitter, and they were weary. They were beaten in body and spirit. They did not want more war, they wanted the quietude of their homes. These were the ones who had left Missouri to wear the gray.

It was different with the guerrillas. It was a surprise to them that the war was lost. They had not been up against the riders of Phil Sheridan, had not faced the guns of Hooker or Meade, the brass cannon of Hunt. They had been fighting the gun-shy State Enrolled Militia, and they were nearly always the victors. When they put down their arms, it was because they had tired of the game, and were ready to go back to their farms.

But a pestilence was upon the land. The blue-belly militia, which had never been ready to turn tail and run, was now the conqueror; and now was their chance to grind the "dirty Rebels" under their heels.

They did their best. They made it illegal for former Confederates to own guns, thus making it impossible for them to hunt wild game—a staple in that land. They requisitioned horses and mules and unhitched them from the plows of former Confederates. If the Southern sympathizers could not farm they could not meet their mortgages and Yankee farmers were waiting to buy up the land. Men who had kept to their homes when the fighting was hot now rode out in bands to burn and kill.

It was called "Reconstruction," and it was an outrage, a legal excuse for murder and pillage.

The men who had seen the big war suffered the indignations in silence. The fight was gone out of them. The guerrillas took as much as they could, then they struck back.

More than any other, two families were the constant target for the militia in Clay County—the Jameses and the Youngers. The boys in both families had ridden with Quantrill. They were not related, but they were friends. Frank and Jesse James; Cole, Jim and Bob Younger. With typical army stupidity, the Federal militia forced these five into the same mold, hoping to goad them into violence and then hang them. But the collusion had the effect of combining nitrogen with glycerine and beating it with a sledge.

The sledge was called the Drake Amendment, the most vicious implement thrust at the Southern sympathizers, former Confederate soldiers and guerrillas.

Charles D. Drake of St. Louis was a member of the Radical Party and of the 1865 Constitutional Convention. In his zeal to have the proposed constitution ratified in spite of clauses that aroused objections in many quarters, he was determined to kill the opposition among his fellow Radicals as well as among the Conservatives. He realized that the convention's adoption of the emancipation ordinance of January 11, 1865, might split the Radicals. To cloud that issue, he bolstered up the desire of the Radicals to "punish" the Secessionists. This was his strongest unifying argument. With it he was able to get the convention to pass an ordinance disenfranchising any voters who could not pass the test of loyalty by signing the so-called ironclad oath:

SECTION 6:

I, ———, do solemnly swear that I am well acquainted with the terms of the 3rd Section, 2nd Article of the Constitution of the State of Missouri, adopted in the year 1865, and have carefully considered the same; that I have never directly or indirectly done any of the acts in said section specified; that I have always been truly and loyally on the side of the United States against all enemies thereof, foreign and domestic; that I will bear true faith and allegiance of the United States, and support the Constitution and laws thereof, as the supreme law of the land, any law or ordinance of any State to the contrary notwithstanding; that I will, to the best of my ability, protect and defend the Union of the United States, and not allow the same to be broken up and dissolved, or the government thereof to be destroyed or overthrown, under any circumstances, if in my power to prevent it; that I will support the Constitution of Missouri; and that I make this oath without mental reservation or evasion and hold it to be binding on me.

Unless a man signed this oath he was not to be allowed to vote, to hold public office, to be a deacon of a church or to enjoy any other privileges of a citizen.

Any Southern sympathizer who signed it would be liable for prosecution.

Drake manipulated the convention members to the point where he persuaded them to apply this disqualification even to the special election on the very document which included this ordinance.

Drake had also foreseen that many of the qualified voters were Union soldiers still away from home. On the last day of the convention, he pushed through an ordinance requiring the governor to send poll books to the army posts (even to those outside the state), so that Missouri soldiers in the armies of the United States could register their votes. Along with copies of the proposed constitution supplied to the soldiers was an interpretation prepared by Drake.

In this way he hand-picked the voters and instructed them in his own bias, while blocking from voting many who had opposed the constitution as it was framed.

To Drake's horror, his own party man, Governor Thomas C. Fletcher, publicly announced that he considered the constitution faulty because it limited the power of the people; it would soon become obsolete; it discriminated against Negroes; and it disenfranchised loyal men.

Drake claimed that the constitution was opposed by still secret Confederates, by disloyal Conservatives, by German settlers, and by Catholics who wanted church property, cemeteries and orphan asylums to be tax-exempt. He launched a fiery anti-Catholic campaign, accusing the Catholic Church of being a "money-getting and money-making machine" which ought to pay its share of taxes. He had a sizable press backing, and even the *Central Christian Advocate* of St. Louis claimed that since the only opponents of the constitution were Catholics and Confederate sympathizers, all Protestants should support it.

It was generally believed that the state's first necessity was to increase its population, and a Board of Immigration had been publishing articles describing to Europeans the advantages they could reap if they settled in Missouri. Now the Missouri *State Times* said: "The outside world is attentively and anxiously observing our progress. . . . Reject the proposed new constitution and our State will be flooded with rebels, and those seeking homes in the West will shun us as a community of semi-barbarians."

Throughout the state Drake shouted: "Every man who hears me knows that, though the organized and armed power of the Rebels is broken, the haughty, rebellious, bloodthirsty heart is not changed!"

His contention was greatly strengthened by the assassination of President Lincoln, and many people openly said that no one who had been connected with the Confederacy could be trusted. Drake made use of this event by saying that it "opened the eyes of the nation to the dangers into which its own big-souled magnanimity was about to plunge it."

The Conservative St. Louis *Daily Dispatch* recalled that Drake had once said, "If President Lincoln should fail to suppress the rebellion, I hope some Brutus will be found to strike him down in a single hour." It was now publicly suggested that Drake may have had some connection with the assassin.

The date of the election was June 6, and its results were not announced until July 1. At first the Conservatives rejoiced that the constitution had been rejected, because of the early returns from St. Louis, where the Germans and Catholics far outnumbered the Radicals.

However, after all the returns were in, it was discovered that the Radicals had won, the out-of-state soldier vote overwhelming the vote of the civilians not carefully disqualified. The final report showed: those in favor of the constitution as framed, 43,670 votes; those against it, 41,808.

The Radicals controlled the government. The men who had gone away to fight for the Confederate ideal, the guerrillas, the Southern sympathizers, found themselves officially stamped as third-class citizens.

In the state of election of 1870 the oath for voters would be abolished by constitutional amendment, and all citizens would once again have the right to register their will at the polls.

But it was still 1865 and former Rebels were little better than dirt.

It was too much for the guerrillas to swallow. Angry men oiled the guns they had kept secret from the militia.

The Jameses and the Youngers, with several neighbors, banded together to fight back in the only way open to them.

Chapter 7

On Friday, February 13, 1866, bands of armed men rode
into Liberty, Missouri, from several directions, meeting in the
square. The leader then deployed his men to strategic points.
It was 8:55 A.M., and no one was in the Clay Co. Savings
Association Bank except Mr. Greenup Bird, the cashier, and
his small son, William. Under threat of death Mr. Bird
opened the vault, and the strangers stuffed $58,000 into a
wheat sack.

This robbery was effected without the dash and defiance of
the holdups that were to follow. In fact, it was executed with
such quiet, speed and precision that nobody knew of it until
it was over. Unfortunately, as a young lad named Wymore
walked toward the William Jewell College, accompanied by a
friend, Henry W. Haynes, he was not quick enough (as
Haynes was) to jump behind a large tree as the bandits fled
the town, firing indiscriminately and yelling with savage fury.
Young Wymore was struck by a bullet and killed.

Several days later the Wymore family received a note,
signed by Jesse and Frank James, expressing regret over the
accidental death of their boy.

David Duncan, who owned a store at Cedarville, three
miles from the James home, met the robber gang after the
Liberty bank had been robbed. At first he said that Jesse and
Frank had been in the gang, but later he said he was not certain—and that was safer for him, of course.

The majority of the Clay County residents suspected that
the James boys were connected with the robbery, but they
said little, taking it for granted that the affairs of the bank
were none of their business. Everyone knew the desperate
character of the Jameses and Youngers; to mention suspicions
might bring about some terrible reprisals. Records indicate
that Jesse James was still suffering from his lung wound for
nearly a year after May, 1865, and that he was seen by no-

body but his cousin, Zee Mimmbs, and Dr. Lankford of Kansas City during that time. Yet people did say a gaunt and sickly-looking rider was among the robbers.

Alexander Mitchell & Company of Lexington, Missouri, was robbed of $2,011.50 on October 30, 1866, during the noon hour, when no one except J. L. Thomas, the clerk, was in the building. On that occasion there were four robbers dressed as travelers—slouch hats and long linen dusters. They emptied the cash drawers and then threatened Thomas' life if he did not produce the key to the main vault. They searched him, but being unable to find the key they left with his gold hunting watch, with covered face, three-quarter plate, English lever, made by M. T. Tobias, Serial No. 4732.

This bold robbery stirred the countryside, and some thought the guilty men were Kansas Jayhawkers, leftovers from the war. Mr. Thomas described one of them as slender and sallow, about five feet seven inches tall and weighing about one hundred forty pounds—a description which fitted Jesse James, just as the description of the gaunt robber at Liberty did.

On the bitter night of February 18, 1867, Jesse was at the Samuel homestead in Kearney when a party of six militiamen rode up to the house. Still suffering from the wound in his lung, Jesse fought them off with a revolver in each hand, and escaped.

Jesse then decided to take an extended tour to get away from his Missouri enemies. Where did he get the money? Did he have a hand in the attempted robbery on March 2, 1867, of the private banking concern of Judge William McLain, at Savannah, Missouri? If he did, he got nothing there, for the alert judge sized up the six outlaws, drew a heavy revolver from a desk drawer and began firing at them, at the same time slamming shut the safe door and locking it. McLain was wounded by the return fire and shortly thereafter his injured arm had to be amputated.

Next, the Hughes and Mason Bank at Richmond, Missouri, was robbed of four thousand dollars in gold coin on May 23, 1867. There the mayor of the town tried to intercept the bandits and was shot four times for his trouble. The raiders, in an attempt to liberate the pro-Confederate prisoners in the jail, killed Jailer Griffin and his fifteen-year-old son.

In the summer of that year Jesse joined his brother Frank at the home of their uncle, Drury Woodson James. The young men were both still recovering from bullet wounds, and they led a quiet life. After nearly a year Jesse returned to Missouri, and within a short time things began to hum. Sometime in 1869 the boys again visited Uncle Drury, then half-owner of the Paso Robles Rancho and Hot Springs, with his brother-in-law, Daniel D. Blackburn, in San Luis Obispo County, California.

Before the death of Harry Younger Hall, nephew of Cole Younger, in January of 1958, he stated that the eight men who robbed the Southern Bank of Kentucky at Russellville on March 20, 1868, were Frank and Jesse James, Cole and Jim Younger, Jim White, George and Oliver Shepherd, and John Jarrette. They surprised this little town of twenty-four hundred people by relieving its bank of fourteen thousand dollars, but they missed fifty thousand dollars because they didn't stop to examine the vault.

For more than a year after that, little was heard about the Jameses. Jesse had raided down in Texas with the guerrillas during the war, and he led the gang down to the Pecos country to hide out.

In the spring of 1869, using the name of Chase, Frank and Jesse took a herd of cattle into Nebraska. A local Frenchman was their foreman.

While there, they married—Indian fashion—two Sioux girls, the daughters of Thomas Wabusha; Jesse marrying Maggie and Frank her sister.

Joe Jesse Chase, in the year 1938, stated that he was born on July 4, 1870; that he was the son of Jesse James. This half-breed also stated that a daughter had been born to Frank James.

The James boys learned that their foreman was stealing cattle from them. Jesse James shot and killed the Frenchman. Then he and his brother gave their Indian wives some money and hurriedly departed.

Chapter 8

It was high noon, December 7, 1869, when a band of armed men invaded Gallatin, Missouri, and rode up to the Daviess County Bank. Several of them dashed inside the building while the others remained mounted, intimidating the townspeople by yelling and shooting their revolvers into the air.

A shot sounded within the bank, and James McDowell rushed out, yelling that the cashier, Captain John Sheets, had been killed by the outlaws. Thomas Lewis, the sixteen-year-old brother-in-law of Captain Sheets, ran into the bank and saw the outlaws pulling Sheets' body from under a counter.

One outlaw dashed to the alley and mounted his horse; but the animal became frightened and jerked away, throwing its rider to the ground and dragging him several yards. Before the townspeople could do any effective firing, however, another outlaw rode onto the scene. The thrown bandit leaped up behind his comrade's saddle, and together they rode out of town.

In the Thursday, January 20, 1870, issue of the Lexington *Register* the following item appeared:

REWARD OFFERED

A reward of three thousand dollars is offered for the apprehension and delivery to the Sheriff of Daviess County of the bodies of the murderers of John W. Sheets, cashier of the Gallatin bank. These murderers are believed to be Jesse and Frank James of Clay County, Mo., and are described as follows:

Jesse—about 6 feet in height, rather slender built, thin visage, hair and complexion rather light and sandy.

Frank—about 5 feet 8 or 10 inches in height, heavy

built, full in the face and hair and complexion same as
Jesse.

These descriptions were inaccurate, Frank was the taller of
the two brothers.

Mrs. Frank A. Fitterer of Gallatin wrote in March of 1952:

I am writing you this letter at the request of my father, now ninety-nine years of age, he feels he is too nervous to write and has asked me to take down, word for
word, his statement. The story follows:

"Capt. Jno Sheets was killed by the James boys at
12:00 o'clock, noon on Dec. 7, 1869. I was just across
the street—16 years old at the time.

"James McDowell ran by and said, 'Sheets has been
killed.' Cap't Sheets was my brother-in-law.

"I forgot the shooting and ran into the bank where he
had just been killed. There was a man in there, pulling
the body from under the counter, where it had fallen after he was shot. While I was in the bank, this man had
gone back into the alley. As he attempted his horse [sic]
threw him and jerked loose in front of the bank. I heard
the crowd holler, 'Catch him.'

"I darted out the door, the crowd was behind the
bank. This man had gotten up on his feet, he saw me,
and drew a revolver. I rushed towards him, he pointed
the gun at me and drove me back. I backed away and
watched until I got out of sight around a corner of the
bank building.

"I then ran across street to Post Office and Chris Gil-
lihan handed a revolver across counter. I reached for it,
but E. Barnum grabbed it.

"We both ran back to the door of the Post Office.
Two men were trying to get on one horse. They left
town, both on this one horse.

"Two or three citizens after them on horse got close
enough to shoot, but their guns were rusty or failed to
operate and the robbers got away.

"They went South and met Preacher Helm, told him
that if he didn't take them by a certain red barn, near
Kidder, a small town, they'd kill him.

"Now Preacher Helm didn't know anything about this

red barn, but luckily for him he struck it just right, and they released him unharmed."

The people of Gallatin did not mind the bank's losing the money—interest rates were too high anyhow, and bankers were generally disliked. But the murder of Captain Sheets was another matter. Sheets had been an officer in the Missouri Federal Militia and had fought several battles with Quantrill's guerrillas. His death cast immediate suspicion upon Jesse and Frank James. Besides, the captured horse proved to be the property of Jesse James, although Jesse claimed he had sold the horse to Jim Anderson prior to the robbery.

On hearing that they were accused of the Gallatin crime, Jesse and Frank rode boldly into Kearney and denied the accusation. However, they were careful not to ride into Gallatin, for there a warrant had been sworn out for Jesse's arrest. The boys' display of wrath and injured innocence was convincing to most of the home-town residents.

Nevertheless, the citizens of Gallatin were not convinced. Armed with a warrant from Daviess County, two men rode to Liberty, Clay County, where they contacted Captain John S. Thomason, former sheriff, for his assistance. Thomason, accompanied by his son and the two men from Gallatin, started at once for the Samuel home. The two men from Gallatin guarded the side of the house facing the woods, while the ex-sheriff and his son deliberately walked up to the front door.

Before the door could be opened the nearby barn door sprang open and the two outlaw brothers galloped out. The men from Gallatin fired, as did the ex-sheriff and his son, but no hits were scored. Over the lot fence jumped the outlaws' horses, with the four men in hot pursuit.

Captain Thomason's horse jumped the fence, but the other animals refused to jump. This left the captain alone in the chase, and he was getting close to his prey. Several shots were heard, and nothing more could be learned until Thomason returned on foot to the Samuel home. There he took a horse from the barn and rode into Liberty.

His story was that when he dismounted in order to get in a good rifle shot, his animal had bolted. However, some time later his horse was found dead in a field. Jesse later stated that when he and Frank noticed that only one man was chasing them they simply killed his horse and let him escape.

Jesse was furious when he learned that the sheriff had taken a horse from the Samuel barn. He wrote Thomason a letter threatening to kill him if the horse was not returned at once, though stating that he was reluctant to do such a thing since the captain had been a soldier in the Confederate Army. The ex-sheriff promptly returned the horse.

The murder of John Sheets had made things hot for them, so the Jameses rode south.

They arrived in Matamoros, Mexico, just in time to attend a public fandango. Jesse and Frank were unable to execute the graceful steps of the Mexican young bloods, but they tried. Their gestures were so amusing to the audience that soon the Mexicans began to mimic the Jameses and to poke fun at them.

This was too much for Frank, and he simply downed the Mexican who was laughing the loudest. A large, raw-boned Mexican reached out and struck Frank full in the face, knocking him into a group of onlookers. Jesse brought up his revolver, and shot the swarthy Mexican through the head.

Jesse and Frank rushed for the door, but it was blocked by a dozen belligerent Mexicans. They shot their way through, killing four of the Mexicans. The others struck with stilettos, stabbing Jesse in the right arm and Frank in the shoulder.

Putting spurs to their mounts, they raced for the Rio Grande. They stopped at Concepcion, Texas, where they remained under the care of a physician for nearly three months.

Returning north, the two young outlaws avoided Missouri and holed up at the home of their uncle, Major George B. Hite, who lived within three miles of Adairville, Kentucky.

Jesse was sick, still suffering from his two lung wounds received in the war in addition to the knife wounds. On top of this came the issuance of the first reward posters, placing a price on the heads of the James brothers for the Gallatin robbery. Jesse was despondent. It was a poor time for Susan James to announce that she was going to marry Allen Parmer, a former guerrilla whom Jesse hated.

In a fury over the prospective marriage, Jesse attempted suicide. He had been using morphine to ease the pain of his lung wounds, so there was a supply on hand. He took sixteen grains, waited for it to take effect, then called Frank and Susan in and told them what he had done.

Frank immediately sent for Dr. D. G. Simmons. It was

seven o'clock in the evening when the doctor arrived, and he found Jesse in a stupor. His pulse was slow, his respiration heavy.

Frank tried to think of something that might arouse his brother. It was necessary to keep him alive until the drug had been at least partially eliminated from his system.

Then the force of habit manifested itself. Jesse evinced powerful excitement when Frank whispered to him certain warning words, suggesting they were in a situation where it was necessary for them to escape or defend themselves. Jesse called for his pistols (which had been emptied) and flourished them while he was propelled around the room between Frank and Susan.

All efforts to keep awake proved futile. By 4:00 A.M., his pulse was reduced to a mere thread, his breathing was feeble and slow. His sister mourned over the bed. Frank sat in mute despair, his eyes fixed upon the floor.

In half an hour Jesse's pulse began to show evidences of improvement, and his breathing became more natural. By six o'clock he aroused and recognized the family, and by the time breakfast was ready he felt hungry. He showed both shame and contrition.

The following November 24 (1870) his sister Susan married Parmer.

Chapter 9

Six years had passed since the scarlet guidons had been trampled into the mud.

There were scars, but for the most part the wounds of war had healed. Time deadened memories, as it must, and life moved on.

In Missouri the Drake Amendment was no more. Crops were being planted and harvested in comparative safety. With a few exceptions, the Lost Cause was being forgotten.

One of these exceptions was Jesse James. Outlaw though he might be, murderer as he was called, the former Confederates were devoted to him. It was through the help of the common man that he avoided arrest. Though he was never the Robin Hood he has been called, there were enough instances of human decency displayed by his gang to convince the people that he was a highwayman, not a thug.

For instance, it is said that when Jesse James and Jim Anderson were once riding through the mountains of southern Tennessee, they stopped along the roadside at a primitive-looking cabin to have dinner. It turned out that they were in the home of Mrs. Charles DeHart, widow of former Quantrillian DeHart, who had recently died as the result of gunshot wounds.

Jesse noticed that the woman was nervous and despondent. He thought it was because she had just lost her husband, but in the conversation he learned that the mortgage on her cabin and land was to be foreclosed that day, and that the amount due was close to five hundred dollars.

"Be sure to get a full receipt for all that you owe the banker, ma'am," he told Mrs. DeHart as he handed her the necessary money. "You say Sheriff Isaac Jones is coming with him to dispossess you? Which direction are they coming from?"

Jesse and Anderson rode off and dismounted along the

roadside. They hid in the brush and waited. In less than half an hour they saw a buggy, occupied by two men, drive toward the widow's home. An hour later this same buggy and occupants came back down the road, and the two men stepped out from the brush.

"Are you Sheriff Jones?"

"Yes. What about it?"

"Throw up your hands!" To punctuate his order Jesse placed the barrel of a heavy revolver near the right ear of the banker, who was sitting beside the sheriff.

"Heavens, man, don't shoot! Here's all the money I've got," said the banker tremulously.

"All I want is five hundred dollars," said Jesse tersely. "Now, on your way!"

There were many other tales, such as the one about the time in Texas when Frank and Jesse came across a family mourning the loss of the father. The Jameses furnished funds for the coffin and gave the widow some money to tide her over. Another time Jesse saved a frightened Negro boy from being lynched, although on still another occasion he was ready to kill a hired hand at the Samuel home for calling his mother a liar. He said he refrained on that occasion only because the man had a large family.

Jesse was now twenty-three. For eight years he had lived by his guns. For six of those years he had been an outlaw, pursued and hunted by the state militia and more than one hundred and five lawmen in Missouri alone. At different times his band had twenty-two known members, but the powerful nucleus was his brother and the Youngers. They ranged from Texas to Iowa, playing havoc with the West's banking system.

On June 3, 1871, the Corydon County treasurer's office at Corydon, Iowa, was visited by a group of armed men, intent on relieving the state of its tax collection. The frightened clerk was unable to open the time-lock safe. When he finally convinced the outlaws that he was telling the truth, they walked down the street and robbed the Ocobock Brothers Bank instead. It had to close down after that, for its capital was gone.

Late in April of 1872 five well-mounted strangers rode into the thriving little community of Columbia, Adair County, in the south-central part of Kentucky. It had a population of about one thousand. The strangers represented themselves as cattle and horse buyers and took up their lodging at the residence of Mr. Green Acrees. They rode around the country ostensibly looking for stock they might purchase, in reality acquainting themselves with the terrain in order to plan their escape after robbing the Kentucky Deposit Bank.

On the morning of the twenty-ninth the five strangers rode up to the bank building. Three of them dismounted and entered. The other two, still mounted, drew heavy Colt revolvers and, with a hearty "Rebel yell," began shooting into the air, telling everyone to get back into their houses.

Inside the bank, seated at a table in the middle of a discussion, were James T. Page, Judge James Garnett, Major T. C. Winfrey and W. H. Hudson.

One of the bandits said in a gruff voice, "Get your hands up, and keep them up, and you won't get hurt."

Judge Garnett started to rise from his chair and let out a cry: "Robbers! Robbers! The bank is being robbed!"

"Shut your damned big mouth, or I'll blow your head off!" one of the bandits snarled, and struck Judge Garnett with the barrel of his revolver.

Mr. Hudson grabbed a chair and swung at the robber who was menacing the judge. The robber dodged, his trigger finger nerved, and the revolver fired. The judge was wounded in the hand.

The third man, who is supposed to have been Jesse James, said to R. A. C. Martin, the cashier, behind the unrailed desk, "This is a holdup, and if you don't want to get your damned head shot off, don't start anything. We mean business. No damn-fool tricks out o' you, or I'll drill you." He shoved his heavy revolver into the cashier's face, saying, "Open up that safe. Be quick about it, too, or I'll splatter your damn brains all over Adair County."

Mr. Martin was foolishly brave, however. He reached for a gun that lay in a nearby drawer. A .45-caliber slug tore through his head and he dropped to the floor dead.

Momentarily distracted by that sudden shot, the two bandits up front looked over, and the four men they were holding at bay ran into the street.

After looting the bank of about fifteen hundred dollars, the three bandits joined their two mounted companions, and the five fled in a southerly direction.

To the south of the town a creek crossed the road. The robbers turned up this creek and crossed a field, where a gate opened upon another road. As they galloped across the field toward the gate, they noticed a man and a boy entering the field. The man swung the gate to its original position after they had passed through, and he was fastening it when the five bandits galloped up and reared their mounts to a stop.

"Open that gate!" one of them shouted.

The man addressed was annoyed by this unfriendly attitude.

"Who in the dodblasted hell do you all think you are, orderin' people 'round like that?" William Canover said. "If you all want that gate opened, open it your own self."

Several of the mounted men guffawed, but the man who had given the order didn't find it amusing. His face flushed, he drew a revolver, and leveled it at Canover as he barked: "I said open it, and that's what I meant. Now open it, and damned quick, or I'll blow your empty head off your shoulders."

Canover opened the gate, saying, "Why, shore, shore, gentlemen, I was only fooling. No hard feelin's."

After that day and until his death Canover was known as "Open the Gate" Bill Canover.

A posse was formed, and Captain J. R. Hindsman, later a lieutenant governor, was placed in charge. However, the bandits had made a clean getaway. Mr. Alexander, president of the bank, offered a reward of twenty-five hundred dollars for the apprehension of the bandits, but the reward went unclaimed. Various descriptions identified the five strangers as Frank and Jesse James, and Cole, Jim and Bob Younger.

On Thursday, September 26, 1872, the James brothers were the main attraction at the Kansas City Fair.

With the Zeiler band of Lexington playing martial music, and an audience of twenty thousand to watch them, Frank and Jesse thundered up to the ticket office at the main gate. Kerchiefs covered their faces and they brandished businesslike revolvers.

To the crowd it was almost like the real thing and they loved it, even though they realized that no bandits in their right minds would try anything so outlandish.

Frank and Jesse rode off with ten thousand dollars and the crowd was amazed at the wonderful acting of the cashier. Edwin Booth couldn't have appeared more hysterical.

On May 27, 1873, Cole and Bob Younger, Jesse James, Bill Chadwell and Clell Miller converged on Sainte Genevieve Savings Association Bank. Jesse and the Youngers entered the bank, while the other two remained outside as guards.

Two men were in the bank—the cashier, O. D. Harris, and a son of the bank's president, General Firman A. Rozier. The robbers directed their pistols at Mr. Harris, telling him to open the vault or die. Mr. Harris sensibly made no attempt to be a hero. He allowed the bandits to relieve the bank of all the cash on hand—forty-one hundred dollars.

The money was stuffed into a grain sack, and the robbers left as quickly as they had appeared. On the road out of Sainte Genevieve the outlaws threw scraps of paper on the road. One of these read:

MARRIED MEN TURN AROUND AND GO HOME: SINGLE MEN FOLLOW.

Another one read:

WE'LL BE IN HERMANN ON MAY 30—COME AND HAVE DINNER WITH US.

The bold desperadoes were true to their word. On May 30 the band rode into Hermann, Missouri, stopped for dinner, and told the residents who they were. There were no law enforcement officers there to greet them.

Chapter 10

In July, 1873, Jesse James offered the thrill-seeking public something new to gasp about.

He learned that a fortune in gold was being shipped via Union Pacific from Cheyenne, Wyoming, to Omaha, Nebraska; from there to be sent east over the Chicago, Rock Island and Pacific Railroad. The site he picked for the robbery was on a slight incline a mile and a half west of Adair, Iowa. The time was set for 8:30 P.M., July 21.

The robbers loosened a track and tied a piece of rope to it, and as the train approached, they jerked the line and spread the rails, causing the engine to topple over, killing the engineer, John Rafferty, and injuring the fireman. The cars remained upright.

When the outlaws rifled the express car they learned that the heavy shipment of gold was scheduled to pass on the following train. The first train robbery west of the Mississippi was a failure by twelve hours.

To reimburse themselves for their trouble, the outlaws sauntered through the train, relieving the passengers of money, jewelry and other valuables. Although there were seven robbers, only Jesse and Frank James, Clell Miller, Bob Younger and Jim Younger were identified.

In the issue of December 29, 1873, the St. Louis *Dispatch* published the following letter from Jesse.

DEER LODGE, MONTANA TERRITORY
December 20, 1873

To THE EDITOR OF THE ST. LOUIS *Dispatch*:

Will you permit me a little space in your columns to say a few words in my own behalf, and in that of my brother, Frank? I know that we are outlaws, and that there is big money on our heads; but even though we were to be hung tomorrow, a newspaper that wanted to give a man a fair chance to put himself right before those who cared for him and whom he cared for, would not hesitate to let him print the truth.

I see from the newspapers of Missouri that one of the Jameses was recognized with the party who robbed the store in Cass County some weeks ago, and that later, at Monegaw Springs, when the prisoners were captured, a James said to a prisoner, "Don't look at me, damn you, for if you go away and report on me I will follow you up and kill you, if it takes me a year."

Perhaps nothing that I might say in the way of a denial would change any man's opinion of me, either one way or the other; but this I do say, that neither Frank nor myself has been in Missouri since the third day of October, 1873, nor any nearer Missouri than Denver City. Neither one of us was in Cass County at the time mentioned, nor at any time within the past year. I am as guiltless of this Cass County store robbery as a child unborn, and knew nothing whatever of it until I saw it in the newspapers.

This proposition, however, I do make, and will stick to it. I made it to McClurg when he was Governor, and he said it was fair and manly, although he did not pay any attention to it, and I now make it to Governor Woodson, who has offered a large reward for my head. If he will guarantee me a fair trial, and Frank also, and protect us from a mob, or from a requisition from the Governor of Iowa, which is the same thing, we will come to Jefferson City, or any other place in Missouri, except Gallatin, surrender ourselves, and take our trial for everything we have been charged with. I do not know that Governor Woodson can do this thing, but if he can and will, we are ready to surrender ourselves. All he will have to do is to give us his word that we shall not be dealt with by a mob, as we would most certainly be if the militia of Daviess County could get their hands upon two of Quantrill's and Anderson's best men, or if the Iowa authorities could get us for a crime that we never committed.

If everything said about a man who had a positive character was true, all the jails and penitentiaries in the country would be full. We have many enemies in Mis-

souri because of the war—many who want to see us
killed if they can get other people to do the killing; but
for all that, if the Governor of our state will guarantee
us a fair trial, we will surrender. If we do not, then let
public opinion brand us as highwaymen, and do it truthfully, for I will never again write a line to defend myself. But surely we should have a little credit in trying to
put ourselves right, and in seeking to have protection
while doing it.

We have been charged with robbing the Gallatin bank
and killing the cashier, with robbing the gate at the Fair
Grounds at Kansas City, with robbing a bank in Ste. Genevieve, with robbing a train in Iowa and killing an engineer, with robbing two or three banks in Kentucky and
killing two or three men there; but for every charge and
on every charge we are willing to be tried. If Governor
Woodson will just promise us protection until we can
prove before any fair jury in the state that we have been
accused falsely and unjustly. If we do not prove this,
then let the law do its worst. We are willing to abide by
the verdict. I do not see how we could well offer anything fairer. We do not mean to be taken alive, and
those who know us will believe this, even if we do say it
ourselves; but we would delight in having a fair trial,
and in having this sleepless vigilance on our part broken
up. Any communication addressed to me at Dear Lodge,
Montana Territory, will be attended to.

(Signed) JESSE W. JAMES

On January 15, 1874, bandits popularly supposed to be the
James gang waylaid a stagecoach between Malvern, Arkansas, and fashionable Hot Springs. The robbers relieved the
passengers of their money and valuables to the amount of
some four thousand dollars. One passenger, George R.
Crump, a Memphis man, had his watch and money returned
to him because the holdup men learned he was an ex-Confederate soldier. As a test they asked him to name his company
commander, the name of the company and some battles in
which he had fought. This stage robbery didn't even make the
front pages of the newspapers.

Another train robbery was planned for Wayne County,
Missouri, near Gads Hill on the Iron Mountain road.

At three-thirty in the afternoon of January 31, 1874, seven

men took charge of the railroad station at Gads Hill, placed the stationmaster under guard, and set the semaphore signal at "STOP." At six o'clock the train came to a stop at the platform.

Conductor Alford stepped off one of the cars and was immediately made to surrender. Several of the outlaws were posted to guard the train crew, while the others robbed the express car and the passengers of more than twelve thousand dollars.

The leader of the band impudently handed Mr. Alford an envelope, saying, "This contains an exact account of the robbery. We prefer this to be published in the newspapers rather than the grossly exaggerated accounts that usually appear after one of our jobs."

Oddly enough the papers carried the item:

> The most daring on record—the southbound train on the Iron Mountain Railroad was robbed here this evening by seven heavily armed men, and robbed of —— dollars. The robbers arrived at the station some time before the arrival of the train, and arrested the station agent and put him under guard, then threw the train on the switch. The robbers were all large men, none of them under six feet tall. They were all masked and started in a southerly direction after they had robbed the train. They were all mounted on fine blooded horses. There is a hell of an excitement in this part of the country.

As a result of the Gads Hill robbery, the famous Pinkerton Detective Agency was hired by the railroad trust to track down the outlaws in Missouri. Allan Pinkerton picked John W. Whicher, one of his shrewdest operatives, to capture Frank and Jesse James.

Whicher came into Clay County on March 15, 1874, and word of his arrival reached Jesse through Jim Latche. Several days later Whicher was found dead on the road between Independence and Blue Mills. He had been shot through the head and the heart.

On April 7, 1874, at seven o'clock in the evening, the regular Texas mail stage, carrying eleven passengers between San Antonio and Austin, was held up and robbed by a band of five masked men. After forcing the driver to halt the stage, they ordered the occupants to alight. Mr. Breckenridge, president of the First National Bank of San Antonio, was relieved of a thousand dollars; Bishop Gregg was forced to give up his money and watch. Courteous to the ladies throughout, the bandits told them to throw all their jewelry and money into a bag or they would be searched. The order was quickly complied with. The total amount taken from the passengers and the mailbags exceeded three thousand dollars. In order to delay the alarm, the outlaws cut out the lead span of the horses and took them along.

The stage did not reach Austin until daylight. A posse was immediately sent to the scene of the holdup, but it was ineffectual after the lapse of so much time. A reward of five hundred dollars was offered for each of the bandits, who were supposed to be Jesse and Frank James, Clell Miller, Cole Younger and Arthur McCoy. One report claimed that Jim Read, husband of the famed woman outlaw, Belle Starr, was a member of the band, but this was never substantiated.

Chapter 11

From the earliest days when Jesse's mother brought him to Kansas City, presumably to die on his own soil, to the height of his notoriety, there was woven throughout the outlaw's career a strong thread of romance.

Recovering from his first serious wound, he was nursed to health by his cousin Zerelda Mimmbs.

She was a young girl in her early teens, but she was frontier stock, and attended him with womanly competence and warmth. She was nicknamed Zee, and from the first it was apparent that she was deeply attracted to Jesse.

In the years that followed, Jesse returned again and again to call on Zee, often risking arrest to see her for precious minutes. The difficulties of their courtship served only to heighten the fervor of their love. Though her family objected to the liaison, Zee could see no other man but Jesse. She knew that he was a hunted man, but she wanted to be with him.

By nature the outlaw is a lonely man. He is harassed and pressed. Movement is his salvation. Trust can be his undoing, so he maintains a breach between himself and all but his own kind. Jesse James was born of the soil, and despite the circumstances forcing the pattern of his life, he retained the basic needs and desires of the settler. He wanted a semblance of roots, he wanted a woman who was his alone.

On April 24, 1874, a month after the Pinkerton detective was found dead, Jesse and Zee were married.

The ceremony took place at the home of Zee's sister, Mrs. W. B. Brander, at Kearney, Missouri. The Rev. William James, Jesse's uncle, officiated. The couple spent their few days of honeymoon at a small log cabin in the hills near Noel, Missouri.

When news of the wedding reached Allan Pinkerton in Chicago, he was furious. The wedding had been an open af-

fair and well attended, despite the groom's being wanted by
the law, Pinkerton knew the situation in Missouri, that Jesse
was being protected by the people in the country; but he was
a bulldog of a man, and was convinced that his man, John
Whicher, had been murdered by the James boys. He brooded
over every minute that Jesse was free, and he went after the
bandit as if his reputation were at stake.

If Jesse's charmed life depended on the help he received
from his neighbors, then Pinkerton knew that the way to
bring him down was to convince the people of Clay County
that Jesse and Frank were nothing more than common
thieves and murderers. He spent almost a year at this task,
pulling the strings from Chicago, and by the end of 1874
there were many neighbors around the Samuel farm with the
feeling that the James boys had stretched the natural sympathy for their troubles during the war.

William Pinkerton, brother of Allan, arrived in Kansas
City to direct the campaign to bring Jesse to bay; and to tie
together all the data received from the spies in the vicinity of
"Castle James," as the Pinkertons called the James-Samuel
home.

In the latter part of January, reports came to William Pinkerton that the James boys had been seen at their home. The
time had arrived. All precautions were taken. Pinkerton ordered that no strangers be allowed to loiter in the Liberty
area and that nothing be done in the least to excite suspicion.
The outlaws were closely watched.

On the afternoon of January 24, several small bands of
men arrived in Clay County and filtered into Liberty long after nightfall. Late on the evening of the twenty-fifth, a special
train came up from Kearney with a detachment of Pinkerton
agents from Kansas City. They were met by citizens well acquainted with the locality and were led to a rendezvous.

Late that night, just past midnight, Pinkerton detectives
stationed themselves at strategic points around the James-
Samuel home. Two men approached the house from the rear,
carrying turpentine balls for lighting up the house. When they
attempted to open the shutters, they awoke an old black ser-
vant, who spread the alarm. Dr. and Mrs. Samuel and the
young children stumbled about in the dark. A turpentine ball
was thrown into the kitchen, and a fire started to rage. Mrs.
Samuel quickly recovered her presence of mind and began to
give directions and personally to exert herself in subduing the

flames. She was permitted only a moment or so to engage in this task. Suddenly another object was thrown into the kitchen. Dr. Samuel thought it was another ignited turpentine ball and attempted to kick it into the fireplace. With the aid of an old broom he finally managed to push the object onto the hot coals and before long it exploded with a loud crash.

In the house were the old black woman and her four-year-old son, as well as Dr. Samuel, Mrs. Samuel, Archie Samuel, Fannie and John Samuel. As the instrument exploded a piece of it struck Archie in the chest. He died before dawn. Another piece of the object struck Mrs. Samuel in the right arm, between the hand and elbow, and the arm had to be amputated at the elbow. She would have bled to death if Dr. Samuel hadn't been there to treat her. The little Negro boy also received a slight wound.

The instrument has always been referred to as a bomb, but it was a potflare, one such as is used on a road or track to indicate that some repair work is going on. It was filled with coal oil and lighted, and the detectives must have thought they would see the Jameses in the lighted room. The top of the thing blew up, but not the bottom. It had a hemispherical bottom made of cast iron, and that was preserved by the James family, giving the impression that the whole thing was made of such metal. The top was of heavy brass, with two tubes about six inches long which carried the wicks. The heavy bottom kept the flare from tipping over in the wind.

In his own writings, Frank James later stated it was not a bomb as such; the heavy brass portion of the instrument flew into bits from the expansion caused by the heat of the fireplace. Even so, it had all the characteristics of a bomb, intentionally or otherwise.

Despite claims that Jesse and Frank were not in the house when the heavy metal flare was thrown in, contemporary records definitely establish that not only were the James boys in the upper room of the Samuel home but also that Clell Miller and Dora and Bill Fox followed the Jameses out through the window.

Jack Ladd, a member of the attacking force, was wounded by the outlaws and later died at Chicago, Illinois. Ladd had been Pinkerton's lookout on the Dan Askew farm, next to the James place, for nearly two years, so as to report on all the movements of the James boys.

Reporters and officials who visited the Samuel home the day following the bombing found evidence that a desperate fight had taken place on the premises and that somebody had been hurt, for spots of blood were found about the grounds. The number of shots fired was said to be from four to twenty. Seven holes appeared in the fence at the northeast corner of the yard, besides the marks of bullets on the fence separating the yard from the house lot, showing they had been fired from the icehouse. Numerous footprints were found at the rear of the icehouse as well as to the rear of the barn. The detectives had attacked in three squads—one from behind the icehouse, one from behind the barn, and one against the kitchen at the northwest corner.

The detectives retreated across the wheatfield west of the barn, leaving an easy trail, plainly showing they were in a great hurry to leave the locality. Drops of blood were found near the stable as well as in the pasture lot south of the house.

On January 28 young Archie was laid to rest in the Kearney cemetery, Clergyman Thomas H. Graves officiating. Mrs. Samuel was too grief-stricken to attend the funeral; besides, she was in great pain because of her injured hand.

At the inquest the verdict of the jury read:

> We, the jury, find that the deceased, Archie Peyton Samuel, came to his death as a result of the explosion from a torpedo thrown through the window of the Samuel residence, by person or persons unknown.

The official report of the adjutant general of Missouri, appeared in the Liberty (Missouri) *Advance*, issue of February 11, 1875:

> To His Excellency, Chas. H. Hardin,
>   Governor of Missouri
> Dear Sir:
>   In pursuance of instructions received from you on Friday last, I proceeded without delay to Clay County, to ascertain as far as possible the facts relating to the recent outrage perpetrated in said county upon the family of Dr. Samuel, the stepfather of the notorious James brothers. Mr. Samuel resides about 2½ miles east of

Kearney, a small town 9 miles north of Liberty. . . .
On the night of Jan. 26th, between 12 and 2 o'clock, the
residence of Mr. Samuel was approached by a party of
men. . . . The party approached the rear and west portion of the building and set fire to the weatherboarding
of the kitchen in three or four places, and threw into the
window thereof a hand grenade.

This instrument was composed of cast and wrought or
malleable iron, strongly secured together and covered
with a wrapping saturated with turpentine or oil. As it
passed through the window and as also it lay upon the
floor it made a very brilliant light alarming the family
who supposed the kitchen to be on fire and rushed in to
extinguish the flames. Mr. Samuel . . . mistook it for a
turpentine ball and attempted to kick it into the fireplace. . . . It then exploded with a report which was
heard a distance of two or three miles. The part composed of cast iron broke into fragments and flew out
with great force. One of the fragments shattered the
right arm below the elbow of Mrs. Samuel, the mother
of the James brothers, to an extent which made amputa-
tion necessary. Another entered the body of her little
son, Archie, wounding him mortally and causing his
death in about four hours.

Mr. Samuel succeeded in putting out the fire in the
weatherboarding and aroused the surrounding neighbors
with the cry of murder. . . . Four pistol reports were
heard by the neighbors . . . but . . . the parties perpetrating the outrage had disappeared. . . .

On Monday, January 26, about half-past seven
o'clock in the evening, an engine with only a caboose attached came down the road from the north and stopped
in the woods about two miles north of Kearney. Several
unknown men then got out of the caboose, which then
continued south in the direction of Kansas City. About
two or three o'clock in the morning, Tuesday, the same
or a similar engine and caboose came from the direction
of Kansas City and stopped for a considerable time at
the place where the unknown men had been left. . . .
The tracks of persons who were stationed behind the
house and of those who set fire and threw the grenade
into the kitchen, were made by boots of superior quality,

quite different from those usually worn by the farmers . . . in the surrounding county. In following the trail of the parties on their retreat, a pistol was found which is now in my possession. This pistol has marks upon it which . . . are identically such as are known to be on the pistols of a well-known band of detectives.

The parties who perpetrated the outrage doubtless approached the house under the belief that the James brothers were there . . . on discovering that they had murdered an innocent lad and mutilated his mother, they deemed it prudent to retire and leave as little evidence . . . as possible. There are no details concerning the signs of the struggle which took place near the barn and elsewhere on the premises. . . .

Respectfully,
G. C. BINGHAM, *Adjt. General*

Public sentiment rose to a high pitch in favor of the outlaw Jameses and Youngers after this bombing. In March, General Jeff Jones of Callaway County introduced a bill into the Missouri House of Representatives offering amnesty to the five boys for Civil War crimes if they would agree to surrender and stand trial for crimes allegedly committed by them after the war. Zeal and eloquence went into the bill but, after a stormy debate, it was defeated. Instead of a bill which became a part of Missouri law, it is now just a curiosity—interesting and tragic, but worthless.

No doubt a deciding factor in the minds of the legislators who voted against the proposed amnesty bill was the cold-blooded murder of Daniel H. Askew on Monday, April 12, 1875. All through the war the Jameses had considered Askew a Union spy, but up to the time of the bombing he had not been molested by the outlaw band. After that time, however, Askew, a Radical, was held in distrust by the James family and their friends. At about eight o'clock in the evening, while returning from the spring with a bucket of water, Askew was shot down within ten feet of his house. Three bullets pierced him, and he died instantly.

The jury at the inquest said: "We, the jury, find that Daniel H. Askew came to his death by a gunshot wound from the hand of unknown person or persons."

Chapter 12

If, as some believe, all men are puppets dangling on the strings of fate, the puppet master handling the Jameses and Youngers was giving his characters a turn—from heroes to tragic pawns.

Jesse's mother had her arm amputated, and his half-brother Archie was dead. It was the first time, since the war, that violence had touched the James family.

On August 16, 1874, there was a wedding at Leavenworth, Kansas. Frank married Annie Ralston against the wishes of her family. The couple went to Nashville, Tennessee, where Jesse and Zee were living. Zee was five months pregnant.

In July, 1875, Cole Younger turned up in Nashville with Tom Webb. He had met Webb in Cincinnati, and together they had hatched a plan to rob the bank at Huntington, West Virginia. Webb knew the country, but they wanted Jesse to lead the raid. Jesse declined because of Zee's condition, but Frank was ready to ride, and Tom McDaniels—a member of the gang—was available. The robbery was postponed until fall on the assumption that the bank would have more money after the fall harvest.

Zee gave birth to a son on August 31, 1875, at 606 Boscobel Street. The boy was named Jesse Edwards James, in honor of Jesse's friend, Major John Newman Edwards of Missouri.

Cole argued that Jesse should join them in the Huntington robbery, but Jesse refused to leave his family.

On September 6, 1875, four well-armed and well-mounted men, dressed in long linen dusters, rode into Huntington and stopped before the bank building. While two remained mounted, firing into the air and yelling to everyone to keep indoors, Frank James and Tom McDaniels entered the bank and ordered the lone occupant, Cashier Robert T. Oney, to open the safe or be killed on the spot. Covered as he was by the heavy pistols, Mr. Oney could do nothing but comply. The four robbers escaped with more than ten thousand dollars in currency.

The pursuit by the enraged citizens, led by the sheriff, was a diligent one. Never before had the outlaws been so hard-pressed. Ten days later they were in southeastern Kentucky, near the Dillon home in Rockcastle County. By that time the exciting news had spread far and wide, and the Dillon boys were on the alert when they saw four heavily armed strangers in the woods near their home.

The Dillons called for them to surrender; their reply was a volley of shots. The Dillons returned the fire but did not know the result of the fight until the next morning. In the woods they found a mortally wounded man who said his name was Tom McDaniels. He was taken to the Dillon home, and a doctor was called, but it was too late to save him. After the stranger's death, a photograph was found on his person, and Mr. Oney positively identified McDaniels as one of the Huntington bank robbers.

Tom Webb was later captured in Fentrees County, Tennessee, and was taken back to Huntington, where he admitted his part in the bank robbery. At his trial he was found guilty and sentenced to twelve years in the West Virginia State Penitentiary at Moundsville.

The gang was inoperative for almost a year. Jesse and Frank were living in Nashville. Frank settled into the quiet existence with his beloved Annie, but Jesse was growing restless.

In May of 1876, Jesse and Frank returned to Clay County, Missouri, and called the gang together.

July 7, 1876, was the day set for the holdup of the Missouri-Pacific train near Otterville, Missouri, at a point known as Rocky Cut; the men whom Jesse chose to help him execute the plans were his brother Frank, Cole and Bob and Jim Younger, Hobbs Kerry, Clell Miller, Charlie Pitts (whose real name was Sam Wells) and Bill Chadwell.

A mile east of Otterville, in Pettis County, there was a track across Otter Creek. In the thick woods on the south side of Rocky Cut the robbers concealed themselves to await the arrival of the midnight train. Hobbs Kerry and Bill Chadwell were left to watch the horses; the other bandits took into custody the bridge watchman and set the lantern in the middle of the tracks, at the bridge approach. When the train came to a sudden halt, the robbers sprang into action.

Jesse James was the first to enter the express car, then came Cole Younger. They took sixteen thousand dollars from the express vault and vanished as quickly as they had appeared. They did not rob the passengers. The train rushed into Tipton, from where the news was flashed to every station along the line and to the major cities in the region.

The robber band rode south until nearly daylight, when they stopped in a wooded section and divided the loot. Then the band broke up and left in pairs, with Cole Younger and the James boys leaving together.

Hobbs Kerry was not used to so much money, and he drank too much during the next few days. At Granby and Joplin, Missouri, he talked about the robbery just before he took a quick trip into Indian Territory to see some old friends. When he returned to Granby he was placed under arrest and questioned in connection with the Rocky Cut holdup. Kerry named those who had perpetrated the robbery, but those members of the band were safe in Indian Territory, for the time being, and nothing could be done. Kerry was sentenced to five years in prison.

NORTHFIELD, MINNESOTA BEGINNING OF THE END

---◆---

1876

Chapter 13

It was early morning, and a thin mist clouded the wooded area west of Northfield, Minnesota. The day was already warm. The woods and surrounding fields were still green, but with the subtle changes of September beginning to show.

Five horses were ground-staked and their riders were hunkered down against the trees.

Jesse James pulled at his thick beard and glowered at Bob Younger. Bob was drinking and Jesse did not like it. He had said something about it, but Bob had answered sullenly, "Don't you worry none about me. I'll do my part."

Cole Younger and Frank James were heel-squatted, smoking their twisted cheroots. Jim Younger idly tossed a knife into the soft soil.

The sound of horses brought them to their feet. Three riders came from the south and slipped into the protection of the trees. The newcomers were greeted and they dismounted. With the arrival of Bill Chadwell, Clell Miller and Charlie Pitts, the gang was complete.

Gathering in a circle, the men went over the plan that Jesse had worked out. When he was finished they mounted and dispersed, leaving in different directions.

Bill Chadwell had suggested they rob the bank at Northfield while the gang was hiding in Indian Territory after the Rocky Cut robbery. He was Minnesota born and knew the country well. Northfield was a busy center of farming and cattle and the bank was wealthy. Jesse had vetoed the plan at first as too dangerous, but Cole Younger had argued in favor of it. The others were feeling their oats after the ease of the Rocky Cut job, and they talked Jesse down. Cole had worked on Jesse's Confederate sympathies, pointing out that one of the bank's major stockholders was General Ben Butler, the scourge of Louisiana.

The addition of Miller and Pitts to the gang, plus Chadwell's knowledge of the country, made the job feasible.

Northfield was divided into two parts, East and West, and connected by a narrow wooden bridge that led into Bridge Square, in the east section. Adjacent to Bridge Square and facing Division Street was the Scriver Block; and near an alley at the south end of the block was the First National Bank. The alley ran behind two hardware stores which were operated by A. R. Manning and J. S. Allen. Opposite the Scriver Block was a group of stores and the Dampier House, a hotel.

The gang filtered into Northfield and melted into the bustle of the early morning. They gathered for lunch at a restaurant on the west side, then Frank James, Bob Younger and Charlie Pitts crossed the bridge and lounged in the square near the bank. These three were to enter the bank when they were joined by Cole Younger and Clell Miller.

But Frank and Clell joined Bob in his drinking, and the plan went haywire.

The moment Cole and Miller appeared on the bridge, the first group entered the bank. Cole, who was an expert inside man, knew that things could go to hell quickly without a restraining hand in the bank, and he rushed forward. Hoping to pull the plan back into shape, Cole ordered Miller to close the bank door, while he dismounted and pretended to tighten his saddle girth, and made a fast appraisal of the street situation.

J. S. Allen had seen the two horsemen galloping up and became suspicious. He started into the bank to see what was going on, and Miller commanded him to go away. He turned and left, but the moment he rounded the corner of the building he began to shout.

"They're robbing the bank! Get your guns, boys! Get your guns!"

H. M. Wheeler, a young medical student, was passing the time of day on the porch of the Dampier House. He took up the cry, shouting, "Robbery! Robbery!"

Cole yelled for Wheeler to mind his own business. At the same time he fired a shot into the air as a warning to the three outlaws at the bridge. The next shot was heard from inside the bank, and then the firing became general. Chadwell, Jim Younger and Jesse James rode up at this time, firing their revolvers and yelling like madmen. One of the pedestrians, a Swedish immigrant named Nicholas Gustavson, who could not understand English and who probably did not know what was going on, was shot in the first fusillade. He died several days later.

The residents of Northfield were quick to man the defenses of their town. Those old-timers who had fought the Indians now sought to drive off this band of invading outlaws. Elias Stacy fired a blast of bird shot into Clell Miller's face. A. R. Manning killed Charlie Pitts' horse with a shot from his breech-loading rifle.

Cole Younger, always the quick-thinking former guerrilla, was ready to call off the robbery. He yelled to his companions in the bank that it was time for a getaway. Cole had scarcely issued the command when a shot from Manning's rifle shattered his thigh. Manning backed away to reload. His next shot was directed at the impatient horseman, Bill Chadwell, who was waiting about eighty yards away. It was a direct hit—Chadwell fell dead with a bullet through his heart. This was misfortune for the gang; they would have no guidance from a local boy in getting out of the state.

Young Wheeler, after helping to spread the alarm, rushed to the drugstore, where he usually kept his gun, but remembered he had left it at home, raced through the store, deciding to get a weapon from a neighbor. On second thought he ran toward the Dampier House, where he had seen a gun. Instead of finding a shotgun as he had hoped, he found only an old army carbine.

Mr. Dampier located three cartridges, and Wheeler raced to a second-story window of the hotel just as the climax of the battle was reached. His first shot was aimed at Jim Younger, but his aim was too high and the bullet struck the ground beyond the outlaw. Wheeler then chose Clell Miller as his second target. The heavy bullet passed through Miller's body, severing the great artery and bringing instant death.

In his excitement Wheeler dropped the remaining cartridge to the floor, breaking the paper of which it was made. Luckily Mr. Dampier had found a fresh supply of cartridges and joined him at the window. Wheeler's next shot shattered Bob Younger's right elbow as the bandit ran from the bank. Bob quickly executed the "border shift" by throwing his revolver into his left hand, ready for instant use.

Bob Younger ran up Division Street, where he mounted behind his brother Cole, and the surviving bandits fled.

The citizens of Northfield rushed into the street, but they failed to take advantage of the robbers' flight by firing after them. Wheeler later explained that too many people were in the street, and to have fired might have endangered their lives.

Cole, of course, wanted to know what had happened inside the bank, and as they rode pell-mell from the town Bob managed to give him most of the details. The first arrivals had entered the bank and covered A. E. Bunker, the teller; F. J. Wilcox, assistant bookkeeper; and the head bookkeeper, Joseph Lee Heywood. Since the cashier was out of town that day, Heywood was acting in his capacity. He informed the bandits that the safe had a time lock and could not be opened at that particular time. The three bandits certainly must have failed to use their heads. Why would the vault be time-locked at that time, past noon? The irony is that, though the safe was closed and the bolts thrown, the combination was not in operation. A simple twist of the handle would have opened the vault.

When Bunker saw an opportunity to escape, he dashed behind the vault and ran for the door. Several shots were fired at him, with Pitts wounding him in the shoulder. At the same time Cole's command to give up the robbery was heard, and the three bandits in the bank retreated. The last of the trio turned and deliberately shot and killed Joseph Lee Heywood.

Riding abreast and racing down the Dundas Road, the robbers fled from Northfield. A posse from the town followed, and the governor—John S. Pillsbury—offered a ten thousand dollar reward for the capture of the surviving bandits, later changing the figure to one thousand dollars apiece, any condition. Other rewards were posted by various business houses in Northfield.

Northfield suffered widespread grief over the murder of Mr. Heywood. He had been a prominent church member as well as a member of the board of trustees of Carleton College in that city. Everyone had respected him, and it was hard to believe that he was dead. On Sunday, September 10, he was buried in the Northfield Cemetery at the south end of the town.

The bewildered outlaws, because of the loss of their Minnesota guide, covered only about fifty miles in five days. Near Mankato they rested at a deserted farmhouse. Pursuit of them had been abandoned but, on hearing that they were near Mankato, searching parties hurried out and officers from nearby cities joined the search. Two detectives came from as far away as St. Louis, Missouri, but the bandits were not found. Some of them had crossed the Blue Earth River while two of them, mounted on a single horse, had passed near Lake Crystal.

It was near Mankato that the Youngers and the James boys parted company. Jesse had coldly suggested that Bob Younger be disposed of; that he was injured too badly to live, anyway, and that he slowed down their escape.

"You're a no-good bastard, Jesse James, to make such a suggestion!" exclaimed Cole. "I ought to kill you for it. I have no quarrel with Frank—he and I have always been good friends. But now you and I have come to a parting of the ways."

"That's fine by me," Jesse said with a pretense of non-chalance. "We'll just let Frank make up his own mind."

It was finally agreed that the two Jameses should go in one direction, while the Youngers and Charlie Pitts should go in another.

On September 21 a farm boy named A. O. Sorbel dashed into Madelia. He said that he had been accosted by two men who seemed to be part of the outlaw gang. They had threatened to kill him if he revealed their presence.

A new posse was formed. It surrounded the bandits in the Watonwan River swamplands near Madelia, who turned out to be Pitts and the three Youngers. When Captain W. W. Murphy called for volunteers to capture them, six possemen responded—Sheriff Glispin, Colonel T. L. Vought, B. M. Rice, G. A. Bradford, C. A. Pomeroy and S. R. Severson. A short but violent fight followed. Charlie Pitts was killed by a bullet through the heart. Jim Younger received five bullets, one of which shattered his upper jaw and lodged beneath his brain. (This bullet was later removed in the prison by a young hospital steward named Clark.) Cole received eleven wounds during the fight, and Bob was shot through the right lung.

When Cole Younger surrendered, one of the possemen wanted to shoot him, but Captain Murphy warned, "If you do that, you, too, will be killed!"

The body of Pitts was carried to St. Paul and turned over to the state authorities.

The Youngers were taken to the Flanders House in Madelia, where their wounds were treated. Later they were taken to Faribault, Minnesota, where they pleaded guilty to the charges against them in order to avoid capital punishment. Judge Lord sentenced them to life imprisonment in the State Penitentiary at Stillwater.

Bob Younger never left the confines of the dreary prison —he died on September 16, 1889, of consumption.

Cole and Jim were released in 1901, but Jim's freedom was short-lived; he committed suicide on October 19, 1902, in the Reardon Hotel, St. Paul, Minnesota.

Cole outlived all members of the band—he passed away March 21, 1916, at Lee's Summit, Missouri.

Chapter 14

With one tired horse between them, Jesse and Frank were
alone in strange, alien country.

A deputy came upon them near Lake Crystal, Minnesota.
He fired at them, causing their horse to bolt. Both men were
thrown to the ground, but it was dark, and they managed to
elude capture.

They stole two horses from a farm and made good their
escape. Riding south, without plan, they decided to part company and meet later at Fort Dodge.

Jesse abandoned his horse and proceeded on foot, seeking
the isolation of the Big Woods country in southern Minnesota.

He arrived at the home of George B. Armes, where in
those days a stranger from the outside world was an honor to
any backwoodsman host. The outlaw explained that he was
interested in buying several farms in the locality and asked
that he be permitted to remain there for a few days.

The Armes family later said he was courteous and soft-spoken and won his way into their hearts by his many helpful
acts. Three of the older boys—eighteen, sixteen and thirteen
years of age—found the stranger especially interesting. They
were intrigued with the cartridge belt and guns which he always wore and which he only once removed in their presence.
One hot afternoon they coaxed him to go swimming with
them in the Des Moines River. He left his belt and guns on
the river bank beside his clothes. The boys were swimming in
the nude and noticed a peculiar scar on the stranger's right
side. When asked how he came by it, he replied that he had
been kicked by a mule.

While they were laughing and enjoying their swim, one of
the boys yelled, "Look out, they'll get you!" He was referring
to his brothers, who were planning to duck the stranger, but
the stranger evidently thought he meant something else. He

dashed for the shore, grabbed his guns and cried, "They'll never take me alive!" When the stranger saw he was the victim of a prank, he laughed and smoothed things over so that the boys thought nothing of the incident (until later).

That same evening the stranger gave Mr. Armes one of his guns as a token of his appreciation for the kindness shown him. He told Armes the gift was in return for introductions to several farm people who had property to sell. The stranger "bought" several farms, but only on paper. He said he had to go into Fort Dodge to get the money to complete the transactions. The Armes family agreed to drive him there in their lumber wagon. Arriving in the town, he asked them to wait on a certain corner for him, while he went to see a friend to get the money. That was the last the Armes family ever saw of the "land buyer."

Afterward the Armes family saw a newspaper, a rare event for them. In it was a picture of Jesse James with an offer of a reward for his capture.

(Mr. Armes later moved to Oregon, where he passed away in 1897. The gift gun from Jesse James became the property of an older son, A. E. Armes, who died at St. Edward, Nebraska, in 1919. Today it belongs to his daughter, Lucile Armes Peterson, who has refused many tempting offers for it. The pistol is a .22 caliber, made by the American Standard Tool Company, Newark, New Jersey; a seven-shot affair with a brass frame that breaks up instead of down, as did many guns in those days. There is no trigger guard, and the front sight has been removed to enable quick draw. The only numerals on it are 272-1.)

Leaving Fort Dodge, Jesse and Frank traveled to Kingsley, Iowa, where they accosted Dr. S. Mosher, making him change clothes with one of them and taking his horse.

Mosher rushed into Sioux City with his dramatic story. On the eighteenth of September he told the story to Mr. G. W. Hunt, editor of the *Democrat*, asking him to spread the alarm. But Hunt, determined to assist the outlaw brothers, took advantage of his close friendship with the police officers and thwarted the plan to patrol the Missouri River, which one ambitious citizen had advanced on the hunch that the outlaws might resort to water travel.

When Hunt overtook Sheriff McDonald, who was on the right trail, he used a little strategy to turn the posse off in another direction. Then he and a friend waylaid Jesse and

Frank near Woodbury and offered to be of help to them. In return they asked for some unknown facts concerning their escapades, so that Hunt could run an interesting article in the paper as soon as the Jameses were out of the country. The boys thought this was a good joke. Since they were not acquainted with the lay of the land, they were glad to co-operate with Hunt.

Because Hunt and the friend traveling with him were so well known in the area, no questions were asked of them as they drove their wagon along the highway. They had one of the Jameses in the wagon with them, his horse tied behind, while the other brother was riding his horse alongside the wagon.

Frank and Jesse asked Hunt to direct them to a place across from Burt County, Nebraska, where some years earlier they had lived with their young Sioux wives. When they reached the Little Sioux, Iowa, near the confluence of the Little Sioux and the Missouri rivers, the editor helped them steal a skiff, and when they climbed into it they waved good-by. Hunt returned to his newspaper office and prepared an exclusive story (without byline, of course) which must have enraged Sheriff McDonald.

The Northfield raid will always remain an intriguing subject. Tourists visiting the town never fail to ask about the battle at the bank. They always stop to look at the memorial tablet on the stone building that housed the bank at that time and the well-kept grave of Mr. Heywood, the hero of that September day. The First National Bank has a Colt's revolver which was picked up in the street after the fight. It is a Peacemaker, Serial No. 11382, has a long barrel and ivory grips, and is nickel-plated. Also in Northfield can be seen Pitts' .44-caliber Russian-make revolver and a piece of his scalp and ear.

A much-debated subject of controversy after Northfield was the question, "Which of the outlaws committed the murder of Mr. Heywood in the bank?"

Some said it was Pitts; others that Jesse did it because he was frustrated at having to leave the bank without getting any money. However, this accusation was not made against Jesse until after he was dead. It is possible that the blame was then placed on him as a protection for Frank James, who was being tried on other charges. Cole Younger had at first implied to officers that Jesse had held the pistol to the bookkeeper's head. In 1916 Cole Younger made a deathbed statement to Jesse Edwards James and to Harry Hoffman, a close friend, to the effect that Jesse had nothing to do with the murder of Heywood. He claimed that Jesse had been in the street and not even in the bank building during the raid. But Cole added, "He who rode the dun horse at Northfield killed Heywood."

Perhaps Cole didn't realize that the mention of the dun horse would one day point an accusing finger at the killer. Charles Kemper, a well-known historian of Missouri, from his home in Independence has reported that Patterson Stewart of Kansas City was a prosperous builder; that his own uncle, George Kemper, was an employee of the Stewarts, lived in their home, and kept his dun horse in their barn. This long-range saddle animal was stolen from the barn on August 15, 1876, and on August 18 Charlie Pitts' brother-in-law, Charles Turner, rowed the outlaw party across the Missouri River near Parkville, and noticed that Frank James was on the dun horse.

It also appears that Jesse's proposition to dispose of the wounded Younger is also true, for in 1914 Cole Younger carried on the following conversation with a close relative who promised that it should never be repeated during Cole's life.

Q. Cole, were the James boys in with you at the Northfield raid?

A. Yes, they were, and using the names of Howard and Woods.

Q. Why, then, did you state they were not and that Howard and Woods were the real names of these other two men?

A. Simply to protect Frank James. If it was thought for a minute that Jesse did not do the killing of the cashier, Heywood, then Yankee Bligh and detectives from St. Louis would have swooped down on Frank and tried him for the killing. But as long as everyone thought that Jesse did it and Jesse was dead, it was left to rest that way.

Q. Who, then, did kill Cashier Heywood?

A. It was Frank James, and to finally answer the question of who rode the dun horse at Northfield, it was Frank James. It was stolen from a man named Stewart or something like that, in Kansas City, I believe it was. He was noted to be a sprinter, and we always got the best and fastest horseflesh we could. It saved our lives many times.

Q. Is it true that Jesse wished to kill your wounded brother in order to make escape a sure thing?

A. Yes, Jesse did suggest this, and I believe he would have carried it out had he been permitted to do so. Frank would never think of such a thing. Frank and I were very close, but not so with Jesse. Jesse and I got along, but as the gang was placed in different categories, we all managed to get along.

Q. What do you mean by inside men?

A. The inside men were picked for their ability to handle the bank robberies from inside the building and took care of that part of it. Others were called street men, those who lingered at the outside of the building to protect the men inside. Jim and Bob [Younger] were good men at that, as was Clell Miller. Frank and Jesse and I took turns doing this. Such fellows as Tucker Bassham and Hobbs Kerry were used only to hold the horses or to frighten citizens away from the locality of the robbery. They were never trusted with any important positions.

Q. Was Jesse James killed at St. Joe as claimed?

A. He certainly was. We Youngers were shown photos of the dead man, and we knew it was Jesse, but could not speak out at the time as it would have linked us with him and would probably have caused our excellent prison record to be destroyed. One of our sisters, I will not mention her name, secretly went to St. Joe and saw the body to make sure, and relayed the word to us that it was Jesse, but we had no doubt of it, as the sands of time just ran out on him.

Q. Do you think a great number of the robberies laid at your door were committed by someone else?

A. There is no question of that. We were accused of several holdups even after we were in prison.

This conversation is verified by the fact that Cole gave a similar résumé to Captain Elias Hoagland of the St. Louis Police Department when Hoagland was just a young detective, several years after Cole's release from prison and when he was running a Wild West Show. At that time Cole was traveling with the James-Younger Carnival in Springfield, Illinois, when he became drunk and was arrested. He was about to be thrown into the local jailhouse, but young Hoagland, who was in Springfield especially to see the show, rescued him. Realizing that such an arrest might ruin the old fellow, Hoagland talked the Springfield police into releasing Cole to him, promising to see that he was cared for that night. He took Cole to his hotel room and put him to bed.

Several days later Cole contacted the young officer and gave him one of his revolvers as a keepsake. Cole also related to his new friend facts about the Northfield raid which he said he had never told before. It was shortly after the Youngers had been released from prison, and the Northfield raid was uppermost in people's minds. Naturally Hoagland wanted some information about it. He has recently told this writer that the conversation quoted above is in substance similar to the one he had with Cole. This should definitely prove that the James boys were at Northfield and that it was Frank who shot Heywood.

Chapter 15

The Northfield fiasco was a blow to Jesse. For the first time the citizens of a town had risen to strike back at him, and he took it as a personal affront.

Riding south from Nebraska, he became more taciturn and moody than usual. In his own mind he had always been the symbol of the downtrodden rising up against tyranny. He had fought the Union, the bankers, the railroads. Now he had the people to fight, and he had tasted the stinging violence of the people when aroused.

Giving Missouri a wide berth, Jesse and Frank rode into Kentucky and holed up with their cousins, the Hites. They made short trips to visit their families, but news of the Northfield disaster was on everyone's lips, and Jesse decided to move into safer territory.

It was not uncommon for the James gang to make fast trips into Texas—to that place known as the Territory of Bexar. At the Rio Pecos, at the foot of the rugged mountains, they had already established a hideaway known to them as the Rest Ranch.

The Jameses were restless by nature, and after a brief stay at Rest Ranch they dared the dangers of the border.

Frank James gave an account of the flight after Northfield in a conversation with Cole Younger, many years later at Lee's Summit, Missouri. William Stigers, of St. Joseph, recorded the conversation.

> I have just returned from a pleasant visit at Lee's Summit, Mo., where I visited Cole Younger and Frank James, the latter having come from Kearney to see Cole and it was my good fortune to see them together by mere chance. We had just returned from the Younger cemetery lot where Cole pointed out the graves of his family members buried there, including John, who had

87

been killed at Osceola, Mo., in a fight with police officers. He had a very pleasant time, with Cole puffing away at his fancy long pipe and Frank nipping the bottle occasionally. Although I visited with them the entire day there was little said about the outlaw career of either of them. However, there was about a half hour's talk about some of Frank's life and I wish to jot it down before it escapes my memory. Frank talked as if in a trance and sometimes I believe he hardly knew I was present. At any rate, here is what transpired. Frank addressed Cole:

"Cole, you know we both would have done different if we had been given a chance. You know that Jesse said many times to Mom that he would gladly wear duck clothes the rest of his life if he could be a free man. I felt the same way at the time and took a chance at the trial and came out free. Once before Jesse died I had a chance to do this, too, it was after our trip to Mexico, you knew we made several trips down there, but Jess would not stand for me changing my life."

Cole wanted to know what they did after Northfield and Frank said:

"Not much to speak of. Jesse and I were both well beaten so we laid low in Iowa for a spell and got some treatment from a doctor, especially me as my wound was really acting up then. After that we went to Hite's home, his father was my uncle, down in Kentucky, and hid out for a little while. But we were still too close to home and the detectives, so right after Christmas of that year we headed for Mexico, with main intentions of hiding out at the ranch. But it was too lonely for Jesse, although I did not mind as I had many books there to read, but they held no interest for Jesse. We then took several trips to some Mexican towns right over the border, and got into several scrapes with Mexican soldiers and robbers. Jesse even got himself shot once, but it was nothing serious. One time we got saved by our own soldiers by mere luck and got a good laugh out of it, as when we were with Quantrill the sight of the blue-coats made our blood boil.

"Well, after Mexico, we came back to Missouri, saw Mom, then went down to Tennessee, taking the main roads and no one bothered us. Down there I got into the lumber business. We liked it fine, me and Ann, and my consumption was not acting up much when I worked outside and took it lightly. We got into debt but some of our fine neighbors agreed to help us, and Dr. Eve wanted to settle the whole thing for us. Dr. Eve was quite fond of Jesse. But Jesse was restless again and wanted us to go back on the road after several years of the first peace we actually had known and the world might have forgotten about us if that crazy drunken Ryan hadn't got himself arrested right close to my home. I knew he would talk if given half a chance even though Jesse accepted him as a good and trusted friend, so we had to run again. You know the rest. It was not too long after that Jesse was killed by Ford and I surrendered to Crittenden."

For three years little was heard of Jesse and Frank James. They were implicated in the Ogallala train robbery of 1877, but the subsequent arrest of members of the Sam Bass gang cleared them of everything but the rumors.

Zee and Annie were both living in Nashville, while Jesse and Frank commuted between Texas, Missouri, Mexico and their homes.

Aside from Frank's attempt at the lumber business, there is no record of the James boys earning an honest living during this period. Unlike their cinema counterparts, these outlaws had to have money for food. A letter signed by Jesse makes it apparent that Rest Ranch was being used for rustling cattle across the border.

FORT WORTH, March 10, 1877

FRIEND:

The boys will soon be ready. As soon as the road dries up, and the streams run down, we will drive. We expect to take in a good bunch of cattle. You may look out. There will be lots of bellering after the drive. Remember it's business. The range is good, I learn between Sidney and Deadwood. We may go to pasture somewheres between there or that area. You will hear of it. Tell Sam to come to Honey Grove, Texas, before the drive season comes. There's money in the stock.

As ever,

JESSE JAMES

In the spring of 1879, the Jameses were in the town of Piedras Negras, a favorite meeting place for rogues of all description. It was about the worst place for a white man to enter, but apparently the people suspected the type of persons they were, for Jesse and Frank were not molested. It was near here, however, that they had a run in with some Mexican bandits, and Jesse received a slight flesh wound in the hip.

In Monclova, a large town in Coahuila, they located a former guerrilla friend who had married a Mexican girl. As was the custom of the country, a ball was given in honor of the visitors, with the leading citizens of Monclova attending. Among the guests were two men who appeared to recognize the James boys—one was a young officer of the Mexican Rurales, the other an American resident of Matehuala. Jesse at once noted their attitude and warned Frank.

Some minutes later the Mexican and his American friend left the party. A brigade of soldiers was camped nearby, and the young lieutenant informed the commanding officer that the notorious American outlaws, Jesse and Frank James, were nearby and that a huge reward awaited the captors. Nearly eighty men surrounded the house, and as the officers entered they demanded that the Jameses surrender.

Without hesitation the Jameses shot and killed the officers and two guards. In the subsequent confusion they escaped and rode to their Texas hideaway with only minor scratches. It was such a dark night that pursuit was out of the question.

That summer the Mexican robber chief of Nueva León, Juan Fernando Palaciois, decided to make a raid into the valley where Rest Ranch stood. With thirty men he raced down the valley of the Pecos, rustling a small herd across the Rio Grande into Mexico. The cattle belonged to the Jameses, and they followed Palaciois. One night, using their old-time guerrilla tactics, they moved in on the bandits, killed a number of them, and put the remainder to rout. Before the robbers could be regrouped, Frank and Jesse crossed the Rio Grande into Texas with the cattle.

The enraged Palaciois followed them into Texas after he learned that only two men had been responsible for his loss. Toward evening Jesse saw the Mexicans approaching; at the same time Frank saw horsemen coming from in front of them. Were they caught between two fires? But Jesse's field glasses revealed that the horsemen ahead were a detachment of Federal cavalrymen, and he hastened to take advantage of them as reinforcements. It certainly was ironic that the Jameses should be rescued by Union soldiers! The brigands were chased back into Mexico, while Frank and Jesse were congratulated for having retrieved the stolen cattle.

Following this incident, Jesse and Frank returned to Nashville.

On July 17, 1879, Zee gave birth to a daughter at the Felix Smith farm, and she was named Mary.

Frank wanted to remain in Nashville, but Jesse was already planning a new robbery.

Chapter 16

At six o'clock on the evening of October 7, 1879, the tiny Jackson County (Missouri) hamlet of Glendale was invaded by a band of eleven heavily armed men. Jesse James, Jim Cummins, Ed Miller (brother of Clell), Daniel (Tucker) Bassham and Bill Ryan were members of the group. Their purpose was to hold up the Chicago, Alton and St. Louis train.

The town consisted of only a few buildings, and it was an easy task to bring the entire population under guard before setting the signals to make the engineer stop the train.

At six-forty-five the eastbound train pulled into the station. As Conductor John Greenman stepped from a car he was placed under submission. William Grimes, the express messenger, hastily tried to hide thirty-five thousand dollars in money and valuables, but the express door yielded before he could find a suitable hiding place. Two bandits jumped into the express car, felled Grimes, and departed with the conveniently sacked money. Pleased with the rich haul, the robbers did not molest the passengers, so the entire event was over in fifteen minutes.

Tucker Bassham, the simple lad of Jackson County, soon appeared to have too much money for one in his circumstances, for Jesse had given him a thousand dollars for holding the getaway horses. This money Bassham buried near his home. Major James Liggett, marshall of Kansas City, was quick to realize that Bassham had taken some part in the holdup, but he deferred an arrest in the hope that Bassham might lead him to other members of the band. When it seemed that this hope would not materialize, Deputy Marshals Keshlaer and Langhorne arrested Tucker Bassham on June 30, 1880, and lodged him in the Kansas City jail. He was brought to trial on November 6 and pleaded guilty. Bassham was convicted and sentenced to ten years in the Mis-

Jesse James, Nebraska City, Nebraska, 1875.

*Young Jesse, aged 16,
September 5, 1863.*

*Jesse's son,
Jesse Edwards James,
at age 19.*

Bob Ford, holding pistol—not the one used to shoot down Jesse.

Zerelda Mimms James, wife of Jesse.

Jesse Edwards James at his father's grave at the James homestead, Kearney, Missouri. The remains were later moved to Kearney Cemetery.

Frank James with his dog Jerry, pulled by Dan, his horse.

Frank James at gate leading to the old James homestead.

The Smith & Wesson .44 New Model No. 3 given by Jesse to Bob Ford, who used it to kill Jesse.

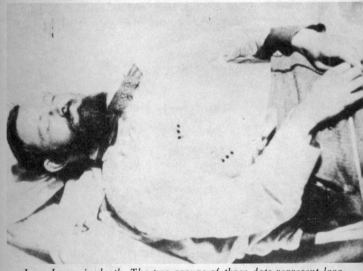

Jesse James in death. The two groups of three dots represent locations of wounds received during the Civil War.

REWARD!

- DEAD OR ALIVE -

$5,000.00 Will be paid for the capture of the men who robbed the bank at

NORTHFIELD, MINN.

They are believed to be Jesse James and his Band, or the Youngers.

All officers are warned to use precaution in making arrest. These are the most desperate men in America.

Take no chances! Shoot to kill!!

J. H. McDonald,
SHERIFF

Reward poster, about 1876.

The house where Jesse James was killed.

Jesse James' gravestone in center, damaged by souvenir hunters, later replaced by a ground-level marker.

souri State Penitentiary at Jefferson City, but later he was pardoned for giving testimony against Bill Ryan.

Tucker Bassham's confession appeared in the November 7, 1880, issue of the Kansas City *Journal*.

"On Monday night preceding the robbery, two neighbors of mine came to me and said they had put up a job to rob a train, and wanted me to go in with them. I told them I didn't want nothing to do with robbing no train, and wouldn't have nothing to do with it nohow; but they kept on persuading and finally went away, saying they would come back in the morning and that I must go with them. They said a very rich train was coming down on the C. & A. and that we could make a big haul, perhaps $100,000. Well, that kinda persuaded me, but still I didn't like to go. They finally told me that Jesse James was arranging the thing and it was sure to be a success.

"Well, then they left. My wife kept pestering me to know what was going on and what they wanted, but I didn't let on to her. I kept thinking about it all night. Of course I'd often heard of Jesse James, and kinda had confidence in him, then I was pretty poor, there wasn't much crops on my place and winter coming on, and I tell you it looked pretty nice to get a little money just then, no matter where it come from. 'Sides, I thought to myself, if I don't go it'll be done just the same anyhow, they'll be down on me and ten to one I'll be more likely to get arrested if I ain't there as if I am.

"Well, I kept thinking it over and in the morning they came to the house early and eat breakfast, and then went out and loafed around the timber and in the cornfield all day so nobody would see them. In the evening they all came in and we eat supper and they give me a pistol, and we all got on our horses and rode off together. We soon met another man on the road, and when we got to Seaver's schoolhouse, about a mile and a half away from my house, they give a kind of whistle for a signal, and two men came out of the timber and rode up. I was introduced to one of them as Jesse James. This was the first time I had ever seen Jesse James in my life. The other was Ed Miller of Clay County."

Bassham said that Jesse James then gave him a shotgun and furnished each man with a mask, and that they all then rode on in silence toward Glendale. No instructions were given to any one man. When they arrived at Glendale, they noticed light in the store, and Bassham was ordered by Jesse James to go in and capture the inmates and bring them over to the station. On looking in the windows he found the usual group of loiterers had left the store and lounged over to the depot to wait for the train to come in. He then went on over to the depot and found the people in the waiting room guarded by one of the men. Jesse James then told him to walk up and down the platform, as the train approached, and fire off his shotgun in the air as fast as he could. The telegraph operator was forced at the point of a pistol, to lower the green light and thus signal the train to stop. Jesse James then asked him if there were any loose ties there that they could lay across the track, and he said he didn't know of any. The men they went and got logs and laid them across the track to obstruct the train if it should take the alarm and not stop for the green light. Meanwhile the train approached; Bassham walked up and down the platform firing off his gun; Jesse James and one of the men jumped into the express car, and Miller jumped on the engine in the manner [with] which all are familiar.

As soon as it was over, Jesse James fired off his pistol, which was the signal for all to leave, and they jumped on their horses and rode rapidly for about half a mile, till they came to a deserted log cabin. Here they alighted and entered. Someone produced a small pocket lantern and somebody else struck a match. Jesse James threw the booty down on a rude table in the middle of the room, divided it out, and shoved each man a pile as they stood around the table. Bassham's share was in the neighborhood of a thousand dollars. Jesse then said: "Now, each one of you fellows go home and stay there. Go to work in the morning and keep your mouths shut, and nobody will ever be the wiser. This country will be full of men in the morning hunting for me and you."

Meanwhile, Frank had returned to Tennessee, but Jesse James was in Missouri, planning the robbery of the Empire City Bank.

Although this was still unknown, Major Liggett at about

this time was formulating plans to capture the outlaw. He knew it would be hard to get any help from the general public because all Missouri was in terror of what would happen to anyone who gave information on the Jameses. They had many stopping places in Clay, Ray, Johnson and Jackson counties as well as elsewhere, yet no man dared report their presence.

Tucker Bassham's wife made this clear after her husband's conviction in connection with the Glendale holdup. She said that Jesse himself told her he would just as soon kill a woman who squealed as a man.

After the Lexington Bank robbery a man who knew the perpetrators was summoned before the grand jury. He gave names and facts. Upon being excused, he made a parting statement: "Gentlemen, I have told the truth. I would never swear a lie." Then he drew his revolver and said, "The notches on this pistol give the number of men I have killed. My life is now in danger, and I desire to say that if anybody is indicted each man on the grand jury can dig his grave." No one was indicted!

Major Liggett decided that perhaps the man who would help him was George Shepherd, former guerrilla, former bank robber and former friend of Jesse James. He knew that Shepherd was working at Jesse Noland's dry-goods establishment in Kansas City, so he sent for him and made him a proposition.

Shepherd liked the idea of helping to capture Jesse James. He was promised a false newspaper clipping showing that he was believed to be connected with the Glendale robbery and therefore wanted by the police. He was supposed to use this clipping as a means of gaining Jesse's confidence. Then, when the opportunity presented itself, he was to kill Jesse James— for which he would be given half the reward money.

Several weeks after the Glendale affair Shepherd set out on this mission. The circulated reports that the James family was at odds with him seem not to have been true, for he certainly was warmly received at the Samuel residence in Kearney. Shepherd told Dr. Samuel and his wife that he was suspected of complicity in the Glendale holdup and, while he had had no part in it, he was forced to flee on account of his previous record. Finally he said he wanted to join Jesse and his gang. They believed him, and Dr. Samuel advised him to ride to a

certain point on the main highway, where he would meet
Jesse and some of his men.

Shepherd repeated his story to Jesse, and of course Jesse
said he was glad to see him. Why should Jesse have enter-
tained any suspicion against George Shepherd? Hadn't they
fought together in the Civil War as guerrillas, and hadn't they
robbed a Kentucky bank together? The party of outlaws returned to the Samuel home and spent the night there. The
next day they went to the home of Benjamin Marr, some
twenty miles from Kansas City. There plans were laid to rob
the Empire City (Jasper County) bank. Shepherd had left
Kansas City with only a small weapon and a very poor horse.
He offered this as his excuse to return there for a better animal and more efficient weapons. Jesse said it was the wise
thing to do and told him to meet the band on the third night
following at a spot in Jackson County known as Six Mile.

Shepherd hurried back to Kansas City, where he imparted
this information to Major Liggett. The major provided Shepherd with a good horse and several heavy-caliber Smith &
Wesson revolvers. When Shepherd reached the Six Mile area
he was informed by Benjamin Marr that Jesse and his men
had gone to Rogue's Island and expected him to hurry over
there. At the outlaw camp he found Jesse James, Jim Cummins, Ed Miller and another man not named.

On November 1, 1879, the outlaws rode to the vicinity of
Empire City, all set for the robbery. Late in the afternoon it
was agreed that Shepherd should ride into town to get the lay
of the land and the exact location of the bank building. It
was after dark when Shepherd arrived in town, and he was
astonished to see a number of lights burning in the bank.
Closer inspection revealed that a dozen men inside were all
armed with double-barreled shotguns. Apparently Major Liggett had already gotten to Empire City, or else he had tele-
graphed the warning of the proposed robbery to the bank
officials.

Shepherd remained in town all night, since Jesse James had
instructed him to do so; then he returned at nine in the morning (Sunday) to find the camp deserted. Familiar guerrilla
signs told him that the outlaws had moved to another location, so he followed them several miles down the road, where
they were all hidden in the brush slightly drunk. Shepherd became alarmed, for he knew that they had not had any liquor
when he left them, and he supposed one or all of them must

have gone into town for it. To add to his fears that his plot against them may have been discovered, Cummins remarked that the bank they were supposed to attack was heavily guarded and wondered why. Shepherd began to swear, but then Jesse James said casually that Cummins had gone into Galena to get whisky and even there had heard rumors of the impending Empire City Bank raid.

"Well," said Shepherd, "maybe the best thing for us to do is get out of here."

They all agreed, and rode south, Ed Miller about a hundred yards to the right, Cummins and the other man the same distance to the left, Jesse James and Shepherd in the center. Thirteen miles south of Galena, Kansas, Shepherd drew rein to slow up a bit, allowing Jesse James to advance several yards. Instantly Shepherd drew one of the heavy revolvers and fired one shot. Jesse James pitched from his saddle to the ground and lay as if dead.

Shepherd reported that he viewed the body for a brief instant but did not fire another shot since the outlaw did not move. Jim Cummins and the unnamed man rushed at Shepherd, pistols drawn. Shepherd's horse was a splendid animal, and before long he had outdistanced the one man, but Cummins kept on the trail. They were both firing at each other and Shepherd received a slight wound in the left leg below the knee. He then whirled his horse, took deliberate aim at Cummins, and fired, bringing Cummins to a halt. Shepherd rode into Galena, where he was placed under the care of a doctor, remaining there three weeks. He told Major Liggett that he was certain he had killed Jesse James and badly wounded Cummins.

Jim Cummins later stated that Shepherd never fired a shot at anyone, especially not at Jesse James. According to him, when Shepherd returned from Empire City he was slightly under the influence of liquor and, since Cummins had already ascertained that the bank was guarded, he and Miller distrusted Shepherd and wanted to kill him. When they saw him riding into camp they opened fire on him, and he fled. That was all there was to it.

It is supposed that the murder of George Shepherd's nephew, Ike Flannery, may have prompted him to undertake the plot to kill Jesse James.

After the Civil War, Ike Flannery became of age and received a legacy of five thousand dollars from the estate of his father. Jesse James and Jim Anderson (brother of "Bloody" Bill) suggested that he accompany them on a little trip. Near Glasgow, Missouri, the three of them stopped at a farmhouse for dinner and then resumed their journey. Shortly afterward the women at the farm heard several shots. Jim Anderson dashed back to tell them that he and his companions had been fired on by a detachment of Union militia and that Ike Flannery had been killed. When the body of Flannery was found in the road, there were two bullet holes in the head and the money was missing.

George Shepherd did not learn the circumstances of Flannery's death until some time later. When he was informed of how Jesse James had acted at the time, he was convinced that his nephew had been murdered for his money. Perhaps ever since then he had longed for an opportunity to kill Jesse James, but the conditions had never been favorable.

Jim Anderson was less lucky than Jesse James. A year and a half after Flannery's murder, George Shepherd ran across him at Sherman, Texas, and they had a drink together as they talked over old times. About midnight George asked Anderson to go over to the courthouse lawn with him, since he wanted to discuss some private business. When they reached the courtyard Anderson, still unaware of Shepherd's purpose, suddenly felt the sharp blade of a bowie knife at his throat. Hurriedly he assured Shepherd that Ike's murder had been Jesse's idea, not his, but Shepherd drew his blade deeply across his throat, and death followed in a few minutes.

Nobody in Sherman suspected Shepherd of the murder of Jim Anderson. Tom DeHart, an ex-guerrilla, had long been known to bear him a grudge, and so strong became the suspicion that DeHart had murdered him that he was forced to leave Sherman, never to return. Not until later years did Shepherd ever tell anyone about his part in Anderson's death.

Chapter 17

On September 3, 1880, Sam McCoy was driving the stagecoach from Mammoth Cave to Cave City, Kentucky. When the stage reached a desolate spot along the way, two mounted men emerged from cover with leveled guns and ordered McCoy to pull up his horses.

The passengers—Judge R. H. Rountree (or Roundtree) and his daughter Elizabeth, of Lebanon; his nephew, P. S. Rountree, a newspaperman from Fairmont, Minnesota; J. E. Craig from Lawrenceville, Georgia; S. M. Shelton from Chattanooga, Tennessee; and several others—were ordered out of the stage and told to place their valuables on the ground. P. S. Rountree shoved his wallet under the seat cushion of the stage and thereby saved his money.

After the bandits had gathered their loot, one of them passed a bottle of whisky around, insisting that each of the victims take a long drink. This seemed to indicate that he was Whisky-Head Ryan. The other robber, because of his pleasant, flattering speech to the ladies, sounded like Jesse James. After a few minutes' conversation the bandits lifted their hats courteously and allowed the stage to proceed.

When the stage reached Cave City, a posse was formed and sent searching along the highway, but without success.

Lieutenant Governor James E. Cantrill issued a proclamation offering a reward of five hundred dollars for the capture of the bold bandits. This reward notice was an incentive for all the amateur sleuths. G. W. Bunger, a deputy sheriff of Ohio County, appeared in Cave City several days later with a suspect, T. J. Hunt, an ex-guerrilla known as Guerrilla Tom. The prisoner insisted that he knew nothing about the Mammoth Cave stage robbery, but his statement fell on deaf ears. His preliminary trial was held on November 20, 1880, and he was bound over to the Barren County Grand Jury. In April of 1881 he was indicted, and the case was brought to trial on

March 31, 1882. The jury returned a verdict of guilty, and Hunt was sentenced to three years in the Kentucky State Penitentiary at Frankfort, Kentucky.

At the very time when Hunt's trial was in progress Jesse James was killed. Jesse's picture was carried in newspapers throughout the country. Judge Rountree instantly saw that a mistake had been made in his identification of Hunt as Jesse James, but it was too late. Hunt had been sentenced a few hours earlier.

The judge used all his influence to correct his mistake and was finally successful in winning a new trial for Hunt. Affidavits were obtained from the two Ford boys, stating that Jesse James and Bill Ryan were the two men who had robbed the stage. Dick Liddil (whose real name was James Andrew Liddil) also made such an affidavit. Another was obtained from Ryan himself, who was then serving a term in the Missouri State Prison for his involvement in the 1879 Glendale robbery. It was furthermore proved that at the time of Jesse's death he had been wearing Judge Rountree's watch and his wife had been wearing Miss Rountree's diamond ring.

As a result, on May 1, 1882, Guerrilla Tom Hunt was pardoned by Governor Blackburn of Kentucky, and that state's legislature awarded him fifteen hundred dollars for the time he had spent in prison.

Frank James had always predicted that Bill Ryan would get them into trouble, and he did. In the early part of 1881 Jesse and Ryan had together visited Frank, but Frank had said, "Jesse, I wish you wouldn't bring that damned drunken Irishman to my house any more. You better keep an eye on him pretty close. His big mouth and loose tongue will get us into trouble when he's full of whisky someday."

"Oh, you just don't like Bill, but he's all right," Jesse assured his older brother. "Yeah, I'll admit he does drink a bit, but he's all right, so stop worrying."

In March, 1881, the Jameses were in Selma, Alabama, residing incognito at the St. James Hotel on Water Street. Jesse was still suffering from his lung wound and wanted to consult a specialist there. On Friday, March 11, at three in the afternoon, United States Army Paymaster Alexander G. Smith rode leisurely along the towpath that paralleled Muscle Shoals Canal, several miles from Florence, Alabama, carrying payroll money for the engineers' camp at Bluewater. Three masked men dashed up and made the startled paymaster a prisoner and confiscated more than five thousand dollars. They forced the unfortunate man to travel with them almost all that night, releasing him many miles from the point of holdup, during a blinding rainstorm. They had removed their masks prior to that and had chatted with Smith in a friendly manner. Smith said one of the men, apparently the oldest of the three, was always quoting Shakespeare and acted more like a preacher than an outlaw. The second was a loud-mouthed braggart who smelled strongly of whisky; the third, apparently the leader, was younger than his companions, talkative and polite, but always extremely on the alert. The trio's description fits the combination of Frank James, Bill Ryan and Jesse James.

Not long after that Ryan, mounted on a fine big gray horse, rode up to the combination general store and saloon operated by Mr. Maddox in Whites Creek. He dismounted and stomped into the place, demanding loudly to be served.

"Gimme some raw oysters an' some o' that thar raw whisky on the back bar."

Ryan was soon drunk, and he began to swagger and boast. Mr. Maddox, though of course he appreciated Ryan's free spending, finally became disgusted at his failure to quiet down this customer, so he called in W. L. Earthman, the owner, to assist him. Mr. Earthman was no more successful.

"Stand back, stand back!" yelled the whisky-head. "Thar ain't nobody in this yere place kin tell me what I kin do or what not t' do. Stand back, or somebody's agoin' t' get hurt. Know who I am? I'm a desperado, thet's what, a killer, that's who I am, an' my name's Tom Hill."

When Ryan reached for his gun, Mr. Earthman dashed around behind him and seized him around the waist. Someone ran next door to a blacksmith shop and asked the smithy, a powerful Negro, to hurry to the saloon. After they had subdued Ryan they searched him and found more than fifteen hundred dollars in gold in a buckskin vest which he wore next to his body.

Though there was no clue as to his identity, the money on his person, plus his boast of being an outlaw, resulted in "Tom Hill" being turned over to the Nashville police. He was "mugged" and his photograph was sent to the principal cities in the country. The police at Kansas City suspected that Tom Hill might be Bill Ryan, the much-wanted member of the

James gang, and William H. Wallace, newly elected prosecuting attorney, identified the picture.

Whisky-Head Ryan was returned to Independence, Missouri, and on October 15, 1881, he was convicted by jury for his part in the Glendale train robbery. He received a twenty-five-year sentence and entered the gates of the prison at Jefferson City on October 16 as prisoner No. 2677. Governor Moorehouse believed Ryan's story that he was suffering from consumption and had not long to live, so on January 4, 1889, he pardoned the robber. Ryan left the prison on April 15, 1889. He didn't have consumption, but he certainly did not live long after leaving prison. He began hitting the bottle again. During one of his sprees he galloped under a tree, struck a low-hanging limb, and fractured his skull in the fall.

The arrest of Ryan at Whites Creek served to widen a breach that had been growing for a long time between Jesse and Frank.

George Shepherd and Jim Cummins have both said that Jesse was antagonistic toward his older brother, and that there were specific instances where gunplay was prevented between the two.

Jesse was inclined to cruelty, extremely vengeful and moody. He had no close friends, but before Northfield, was drawn to Clell Miller; and afterward, to Ryan. Both men were followers who bolstered Jesse's ego.

It was apparent that Ryan would talk, so the Jameses had to move. Frank wanted to get away from Jesse, and he went to Baltimore. Jesse went back to Missouri and began planning a new robbery. When he was ready he sent for Frank and, as usual, Frank returned.

At six-thirty on the afternoon of July 15, 1881, the Chicago, Rock Island and Pacific train left Kansas City and proceeded as far as Cameron, where four passengers boarded the cars. The train was in the charge of Conductor William Westfall; the express messenger was Charles Murray, and Mr. Wolcott was the engineer. At nine-thirty the train reached Winston, where three more passengers boarded her, together with several stonemasons, one of whom was Frank McMillen, in some reports referred to as John McCulloch. These stonemasons were in the employ of the railroad, and it was their function to repair and build piers along the creeks and gulleys. It was not unusual for them to board the train at any point for a free ride to another point of work.

Three of the seven men who had boarded the train at the last two stops rode in the smoking car; two were on the rear platform of the baggage car (in front of the smoking car); the other two took their stand on the front platform of the baggage car, keeping an eye on the fireman and the engineer. Evidently their plan was to rob the express car while the train was in motion and to jump off while it slackened speed near a creek a mile from Winston.

The train had hardly pulled out of the Winston depot when Conductor Westfall began taking up the tickets of the passengers in the smoking car. Suddenly a large man, heavily bearded and wearing a long linen duster, jumped up and cried out, "All aboard!" Apparently that was the prearranged signal for action. At once he shot Westfall in the shoulder, and when Westfall turned to flee, the same man fired again but missed. Then another of the robbers fired the shot that killed Westfall as he staggered out to the platform and rolled off the train to the ground.

McCulloch (or McMillen) tried to get out of the baggage car as the robbers entered. Thinking he was bent on giving the alarm, they shot him dead and pushed his body off the train. Probably this murder was not intentional; yet it may have been intended as a warning to the passengers as to what would happen to them if they interfered. It may also have been a meaningless brushing away of a momentary impediment. John McCulloch (or Frank McMillen) was buried at his home in Wilton Junction, Iowa.

During the melee someone pulled the stop cord, and Engineer Wolcott brought the train to a halt, but he was quickly forced, under threat of instant death, to get it into motion again.

When Charles Murray, in charge of the express company's safe, heard the shooting he guessed the cause of it. He hurried to close the door to the express car but before he could do so several of the bandits shouldered their way in and threatened him with their heavy pistols. He was forced to let them take the keys to the safe. They stuffed the money into an old sack, but grumbled in disappointment at finding only six hundred dollars.

About a mile from Winston the robbers stopped the train, got off and hurried into the woods. There they hastily mounted their hidden horses, not delaying to untie the leather straps which had held them. The remains of the cut reins were later found on tree trunks and kept as souvenirs of the Winston robbery.

Also, in the underbrush near Sibley's Landing on Big Dog Creek, a short distance from the scene, a crumpled piece of paper was found. This proved to have been dropped by one of the robbers, for it read:

KANSAS CITY, July 12, 1881

CHARLEY:—

I got your letter today, and was glad to hear you had got everything ready in time for the 15th. We will be on hand at the time. Bill will be with me. We will be on the train. Don't fear. We will be in the smoker at Winston. Have the horses and boys in good fix for fast work. We will make this joust on the night of the 16th. All is right here. Frank will meet us at Cameron. Look sharp and be well fixed. Have the horses well gaunted. We may have some running to do. Don't get excited, but keep cool till the right time. Wilcox or Wilcott will be on the engine. I think it best to send this to Kidder. Yours till and through death.

SLICK

Why was Westfall deliberately killed? Some said that it was he who had operated the engine which carried Pinkerton detectives to the Samuel residence on the night the bomb was tossed into the kitchen. Certainly it was common belief that Jesse James was the leader of the outlaw band and wanted to slay Westfall in revenge for the bombing; that Frank James was the second who shot him. However, railroaders deny that Westfall had any connection with the Pinkerton affair. On July 17, 1881, William H. Westfall was buried at Plattsburg, Missouri, where his widow and two young sons and one young daughter were living.

The law enforcement officers were able to draw the following descriptions from people who had seen the strangers near Winston about sundown on the day of the robbery, as well as from train passengers:

1. Big bay gelding, heavy mane and tail, about sixteen hands high. (John Samuel, Jesse's half-brother, owned this animal and stated later that Jesse had

been riding him that summer.) Rider was tall, heavy, erect, high cheekbones and broad face, darkish whiskers all over his face, dark hair, good talker. Was this Jesse James?

2. A little bay gelding (the one stolen by Frank James and Dick Liddil in Ray County, Wood Hite's horse). Rider was about thirty, average height, stoop-shouldered, light-complexioned, inclined to heavy build, not much whiskers, very slouchy, said little. Was this Wood Hite?

3. A sorrel gelding, about fifteen and a half hands high, ordinary mane and tail, collar marks, no blaze in face (Lamartine Hudspeth's horse, ridden by Dick Liddil). Rider was about thirty, dark-complexioned, dark hair, dark whiskers, short and round face, average build and height. Was this Dick Liddil?

4. A tall sorrel, stolen from a man named Matthews, most noticeable of all, blaze face, light mane and tail, white hind feet, sixteen hands high (Clarence Hite's horse). Rider was tall, slender, light-complexioned, about twenty years old, front teeth bad and prominent, fuzzy whiskers. Was this Clarence Hite?

5. A little light bay mare, stolen by Frank James and Liddil in Ray County, shod by blacksmith Potts at Liberty, and identified while in possession of Sheriff Timberlake. Rider described as slender man thirty-five to forty, light-complexioned, with light burnsides whiskers, intelligent, good talker, neat in dress. Talked about Ingersoll and quoted Shakespeare. Was this Frank James?

It was not very long before there were new activities by the same gang.

On Tuesday morning, September 6, 1881, when Conductor Hazelbaker of the Chicago and Alton road left Chicago, he little realized that in a short while he would be the object of nationwide conversation. His train made a brief stayover at St. Louis, and at nine on the evening of September 7 it was in the region of Glendale, Missouri, the scene of the recent holdup. Passengers were discussing the robbery, when suddenly the train was brought to a standstill in a deep ravine called Blue Cut, a spot where the Missouri-Pacific line crossed the Chicago and Alton track. The people glanced at each other, wondering what was the matter. Was it a holdup? Surely not so soon on the heels of the other!

Instantly the four cars were boarded by twelve masked men. Engineer L. Foote was first accosted and ordered down from his engine. He and the fireman, John Steading, quickly complied with the order, in view of the deadly revolvers. The express messenger, Mr. Fox, scented danger the moment the train stopped, and he jumped from his car to hide in the weeds along the track. The leader of the robbers, who wore a white cloth with eyeholes over his face, yelled that he would kill Foote if Fox did not reappear and hand over the vault key. Fox came back and was knocked down and rendered unconscious. The leader showed his annoyance when he found only about twenty-five hundred dollars in the express company safe.

As the other robbers entered the passenger cars, one of them cried out, "We are coming in and going through you all, so be damned quick about getting out your money, and don't try to hide any of it."

Just a moment earlier Conductor Hazelbaker and the brakeman, Mr. Burton, had hastily advised the passengers to hide whatever valuables they could. That was a courageous act on their part, but an even more courageous one was their daring of the bandit guns as they walked back along the track to flag down an approaching freight train. If it had been allowed to crash into the stopped passenger train, a number of lives would have been lost. Later Mr. Hazelbaker had this to say:

When I reached the sleeper I told Burton, my brakeman, to flag the train following. I knew there was a freight right after me, and would wreck my train, and I knew that that train must be stopped. Burton said he did not like to go, but the brave fellow went just the same. We dropped off together, and they began to fire at us. Shots whistled all around us. I think there were probably twenty shots fired at us altogether. We finally succeeded in flagging the freight train just in time, and I went back, and, climbing aboard the sleeper, took a back seat and waited quietly to be robbed.

Hazelbaker further said that the gang cursed a great deal and seemed to center their rage on him. The leader, who said he was Jesse James, put a pistol under the conductor's nose and said, "Damn you, smell of that, that's the pistol I shot Westfall with at Winston!"

The leader then made it more than clear that he was incensed by the fact that recent high rewards had been offered for the James gang: "Now, listen, all you dogs, the next reward that is offered we'll burn your damned train, and don't you forget it. We will cut the Pullman loose and save it, because Pullman is white and never offered a reward like you damn railroads and the no-good governor of Missouri. But we'll make a bonfire of your train sure as you live."

When Hazelbaker was later asked what he thought of their attitude, he said: "From their talk it appeared that the robbery was a piece of daredeviltry in revenge for the Winston reward being offered. They constantly shoved pistols under my nose and reminded me of Westfall's fate. After they left we pulled out, and as quick as we could."

"How many were there?" he was asked.

"There were six in the sleeper and four or five outside."

"Did they expose themselves?"

"Not at all. I could see their forms, but absolutely nothing of their features. The leader, supposed to be Jesse James, had on a white muslin cloth with holes cut in it around his head, as if he had made a mask out of a handkerchief. The others wore dirty cloth masks. They were all slender men except the leader, who was a tall, well-built man."

"Could you identify any of them?"

"No, and there lies the trouble."

"How much money do you suppose they got?"

"I could not tell. They took from each passenger between one dollar and three hundred dollars, and maybe got a couple thousand that way. I don't know how much was in the express car."

From all available figures it appears that the robbers obtained about twenty-five hundred dollars from the express car and from three to four thousand in money and jewelry from the passengers.

Messenger Fox made this statement:

When they had robbed the safe of everything, I ran back into the smoking car and hid most of my money. The robbers came in and ordered me, with an oath, to lie down. I did so, and they shoved a gun up to my head and told me to fork over. I said my money was under the cushion. They told me to get it, and I got it in a hurry, you bet. It was somewhere in the neighborhood of fifteen dollars.

Several of the women fainted during this robbing, but water was thrown into their faces and they were told to hand over their money.

Engineer Foote's testimony should not be overlooked:

Between three and four miles east of Independence is a deep cut, over which the Missouri-Pacific track crosses the Chicago and Alton, and it was just before entering the deepest part of this cut that I saw a pile of stones, probably five feet high, on the top of which was a stick, to which was attached a red rag, and behind the whole stood the leader of the robbers. Of course I stopped. I was then approached by four of the gang, besides the leader, who said, "Step down off that engine, and do as I tell you, or I will kill you." He then told me to get the coal pick, which I did, and after some parleying, but as a revolver was pointed at my head I could not refuse to obey.

They then marched myself and John Steading, the fireman, to the express car, and ordered me to break the door down, which I did. Messenger Fox had hidden in the weeds by the roadside, but they swore they would kill me if he didn't come out, and so I called for him and he entered the car with two of the robbers who forced him to open the safe and pour the contents into a sack.

They seemed disappointed in not getting more booty, and knocked Fox down twice with the butt of a navy revolver, cutting his head in a fearful manner. Then they marched us to the coaches, where they kept us covered with revolvers while they robbed the passengers. After the last car was gone through they marched us back to the engine, when the leader said, "Now, get back there, we will remove the stones. You have been a bully boy and here is a little present for you," and he handed me two silver dollars. I told them that I would remove the obstructions, and the entire gang skipped over the embankment, and were out of sight in a twinkling.

In going through the passengers, each one was made to hold up his hands, and what was taken from them was put into a two-bushel sack, which was nearly full of watches, money, and other valuables. They didn't take anything from me.

The train was stopped only a car length off. When I came back one of the robbers said, "Have you lost anything?" I replied, "Fifty cents." He gave me $1.50 for interest. Then I heard one of the robbers say, "Choppy Foote, you're too good a man to keep up this business. Here's two dollars to buy a drink in the morning, and drink it for Jesse James. I warn you, you'll be killed if you don't leave this road. We are going to tear up and burst the Alton and Rock Island roads, for they have been offering rewards for us. We've no grudge against the Pullmans, and will switch off their cars and burn the rest. I am the man who killed Westfall at Winston. He was too smart and drew a revolver."

Matt Chapman, first to be arrested in connection with the Blue Cut robbery, stated that Jesse and Frank James were there. Later, Dick Liddil stated that the Jameses were there with Jim Cummins, Wood Hite, Clarence Hite, Andy Ryan, Ed Miller and Matt Chapman. On March 27, 1882, John Bugler, a citizen of Cracker Neck, Missouri, was arraigned at Independence on suspicion of being a member of the Blue Cut bandit gang. John Land, also under indictment in the same case, made a full confession and implicated those named, as well as Robert and Charley Ford.

Chapter 18

The Blue Cut robbery was the last for Jesse James. The strings of his life were being pulled together, and fate was preparing a martyrdom for him.

Frank's chest was bothering him, and he took his family to live at Rest Ranch in Texas.

Jesse moved his family to Kansas City, where they rented a neat frame house on Woodland Avenue, under the name T. J. Jackson. Never content to live in one house for any length of time, Jesse moved again on September 13 to East Ninth Street, just east of Woodland Avenue. On November 5, 1881, he moved his family to St. Joseph.

During this period the plot to destroy Jesse was being brewed. There were many people involved, but the tools of assassination were two insignificant petty thieves, Charles Wilson Ford and his younger brother, Robert Newton Ford, the sons of J. T. Ford.

Both boys had been raised in early years in Fauquier County, Virginia. Charley was born on July 9, 1857, Bob on January 31, 1862, both in Clark County, Missouri. Other children in the Ford family were Elias Capline (Cap) Ford, born in Missouri; Martha Ford, and Amanda Ford, born in 1855. In 1871 the family moved to Clay County, Missouri, and in 1877 to a farm near Richmond, Ray County. The elder Ford had a brother named William, who married Artella, a sister of Jim Cummins, and went to live on what was known as the Cummins place, a farm near Kearney. Bill Ford simply took over the Cummins place. He had one son named Albert, a cousin to Charley and Bob Ford.

In the summer of 1879 the widowed sister of the Fords, Martha Bolton, rented the old Harbison place near Richmond, where she, Bob and Charley pretended to do farming. Many people in the vicinity suspected the Ford boys of being thieves, but no proof was available. According to Charley, it was here in August of 1879 that he first met Jesse James with Ed Miller. At that time Jesse was introduced as a gambler named Jackson, and he made a favorable impression. As time went on Jesse made several trips to the Harbison place, perhaps to determine whether Charley and Bob were likely prospects as recruits. His last visit there occurred shortly before the Blue Cut robbery.

While living in St. Joseph Jesse became more and more irritable and difficult to get along with. He knew that Ed Miller and "Windy" Jim Cummins had been talking about the Blue Cut robbery. One dark night he surprised Ed Miller in Saline County and killed him. The body was not found for several months, and then it was almost unrecognizable. In fact, many claimed it was the body of Jim Cummins, but Jim soon showed up and, like Mark Twain, said that "reports of his demise had been somewhat exaggerated." It was Jim who said the body was that of Ed Miller; furthermore, he was positive that Jesse James had killed him.

Jesse decided to shut Windy Jim's big mouth and figured one sure way to keep him from talking was to kill him. Jim, however, hightailed it into Arkansas. Jesse and Dick Liddil were right on his trail, so he doubled back into dear old Missouri. He rested at Bill Ford's for several days, then on a hunch saddled his horse and left. He had scarcely turned a bend in the road when Jesse and Liddil rode up to the farmhouse.

Bill wasn't at home, but his wife and fourteen-year-old son Albert were. Jesse inquired about Jim Cummins and was told that he hadn't been there for some time. Not at all satisfied that he was getting the truth, Jesse took young Albert out into the woods and tried to torture information out of him. Neither Liddil nor Jesse could pry anything from the brave lad. Cummins escaped, to end his days peacefully in the Confederate Home at Higginsville, Missouri, where he passed away in 1926.

Jesse's torture of young Albert Ford was one reason his cousin Bob decided to turn against Jesse. Another deciding factor was the killing of Jesse's favorite cousin, Robert Woodson Hite (commonly called Wood), son of George Hite, Sr., of Adairville, Kentucky. In 1878 Major George Hite, Sr., had married the charming young widow Peake, after the death of his first wife. The entire Hite family protested against the marriage, and most of them left the house when she entered it. Within the year she deserted the major.

This stepmother hated Wood Hite and made no bones about it. Shortly afterward Liddil became a member of the gang and went to Kentucky to hide out with Jesse James after one of their escapades. Liddil, a typical backwoodsman of the Cracker Neck region of Missouri, considered himself something of a ladies' man, and the sprightly young Mrs. Hite did not repulse his advances. Wood Hite told Liddil in no uncertain terms to leave his father's wife alone or there would be trouble. Interference of other gang members prevented gunplay between the two one day in the barn lot of the Hite farm. Liddil hurried back to Missouri.

Wood confronted his stepmother with an accusation that she was playing fast and loose with his father, and she retorted that she wasn't entirely unaware of his connection with the James gang. She warned him that if he meddled with her clandestine love affairs she would tell the officers about him.

One day Wood intercepted a Negro named John Tabor as he was carrying a note to one of young Mrs. Hite's admirers. Wood took the note and told Tabor that if he ever caught him on such an errand again he would kill him. The Negro was badly frightened, but again the woman induced him to act as her messenger. Wood caught him, searched him, found another love note, and simply took out his revolver and killed Tabor. He dragged the body into a fence corner and covered it with brush. Several days later it was hardly recognizable because the hogs running loose in the field had found it.

Mrs. Hite swore out a warrant for Wood's arrest, and declared she had witnessed the killing of the Negro. Wood, unaware of this, was fishing in the small creek that ran through his father's farm when two officers from Russellville drove up one afternoon in a buggy. At that time the police had no suspicion that either Wood or Clarence Hite was a member of the famous Jesse James gang. Their occasional possession of a good deal of money had not excited comment because Major Hite, their father, was known to be pretty well fixed.

When the two officers drew up in front of the Hite house in their buggy, no one was at home except Clarence, or "Jeff" as everybody called him. Jeff was a younger brother of Wood, a stoop-shouldered consumptive, a half-wit of nineteen.

"Where's Wood?" one of the officers inquired.

"Down on the creek a-fishin'," Jeff replied.

The officers had no difficulty in locating Wood, and they told him they had come out to get him to go bird hunting with them. Wood, entirely unsuspicious, told them he would go to the house after his shotgun. They started up the path toward the house, walking single file, Wood between them. About halfway to the house the officer in the rear eased a gun into Wood's back.

"Get y' hands up, Wood, an' keep 'em up. You're that bird we aire lookin' for. We've got a murder warrant agin ye."

When Marshal Jeter arrived in Russellville with his prisoner, he placed Wood in an upstairs room of the city's hotel instead of placing him in jail. Of course, a guard was left at the door of the room, but in some unexplainable manner Wood simply walked out. He went down the stairs, through the hotel lobby, out the front door, and mounted a horse conveniently waiting in front of the hotel. He even rode around town for a while, offering a hundred dollars' reward for the return of his "guard."

Several old-timers who personally knew the Fords have reported that Wood, after his "escape" from the hotel prison, went to Missouri, where, on December 4, 1881, he walked into the Ford home in Ray County.

Martha Bolton had just gotten up and was preparing breakfast in the lean-to kitchen, and Elias Capline Ford was out feeding the stock. After the first greeting, Wood inquired if any of the boys were about.

"Charley and Bob and Dick are asleep upstairs," said Martha.

"That dirty Liddil!" Hite exclaimed. "He's got a helluva nerve to hang around after stealing that money out of the bag before it was divided after the Blue Cut job."

Martha told him, "Dick knows you're accusing him of that, and he's mad at you."

"I don't give a damn, and I'll tell Liddil to his face!" cried Wood. "There's been a lot of talk among us about the way he filched that money."

Martha tried to dissuade Wood from openly accusing Liddil. "It will only cause trouble. Don't go upstairs and start a ruckus."

But Hite would not listen to her. He stomped up the stairs and into the bedroom, where two beds stood. In one slept the two Fords and in the other Liddil.

Dick Liddil was a native Missourian about thirty-five years old and as daring as any of the band. He was five feet eight inches tall, with blond hair and a blond mustache, pale blue eyes and a short nose. Two of his brothers, James and John, had ridden with the Jameses during the Civil War and both had been killed.

Wood awoke the three men and addressed Liddil angrily: "You've a damned nerve speaking to me after all the lies you've been a-spreading."

With that Liddil drew a pistol from under his pillow, and the shooting became general. Bob Ford saw that Liddil was wounded in the leg, so he took a shot at Wood Hite. The bullet struck him in the head and killed him. Charley Ford did not get in on the affray; he had been sleeping on the wall side of the bed and quickly jerked up a window and jumped out onto the roof of the lean-to. There were several inches of snow on the roof and Charley slid to the ground, severely spraining his hip and ankle.

Elias Ford was called in to help get rid of Hite's body, because Liddil was wounded and Charley Ford was hurt. So Elias and Bob Ford dug a shallow grave into which they threw Hite's body, wrapped in a dirty horse blanket.

Now the Fords had another reason to want to get rid of Jesse James: they knew what would happen to them when he learned that his favorite cousin had been murdered by Bob's shot. However, Jesse never did learn of Wood's demise. The body was not recovered until April 5, 1882, in an old spring several hundred yards from the Ford residence, covered with a slight sprinkling of earth and some stones. It was nude, and the features were almost unrecognizable. On the right side of the head was a bullet wound, and there was also a wound in the right arm.

At the inquest on April 6 Martha Bolton gave a different version of the killing:

> I recognize the body before me as that of a man who frequently went by the name of Robert Grimes, but his real name was Wood Hite. He was killed in the house in which I live about the last of November or first of December 1881; I do not know who killed him, though I was present when he was shot; it occurred between seven and eight o'clock on a Sunday morning. I had prepared breakfast and called the boys into the dining room; there

were present Dick Liddil, Bob, Wilber (Charley Ford), and Capline Ford, Wood Hite, and my little daughter. There had been a difficulty between Liddil and Hite a few months previously in Kentucky, but they appeared friendly while at my house until the shooting occurred. My back was toward the two men when they commenced shooting in the dining room, but I quickly turned and saw Liddil and Hite, the former standing near the kitchen door and the latter perhaps ten feet distant, on the east side of the room. Three or four shots were fired so quickly that the room filled with smoke and I could not even see the men, but there were perhaps as many as ten shots fired in all. When the firing ceased I saw Wood Hite lying on the floor dead, and Liddil was holding his hand over a wound in his hip, from which the blood was flowing freely. Hite was shot in the head and must have died instantly. I do not know whether Robert fired at Hite or not, but his pistol was in his hand and I suppose he shot at Hite one or more times. After the killing my brothers carried the body upstairs and left it there until after night, when Capline and Charles Ford wrapped the body in the blanket and carried it out of the house to the place where it was found. Liddil was badly hurt and was assisted to a bed upstairs in the north room.

Besides the burgeoning hatreds that were flaring up around Jesse James, the lure of wealth was added to the fire of deceit.

During Governor Hardin's administration nearly all the rewards for the Jameses offered by the state of Missouri were withdrawn, and when Governor Phelps took office he withdrew all the remaining offers. This caused the various corporations to withdraw any rewards they had offered, and for some time the Jameses were without a price on their heads.

However, when Governor T. T. Crittenden took over the governorship, he called to a meeting at the Southern Hotel in St. Louis representatives from the regions through which the principal roads ran into Kansas City and St. Louis. The result of this conference was the governor's proclamation that fifty-five thousand dollars would be awarded to anyone effecting the capture of the entire robber band, or five thousand dollars for the arrest and conviction of any separate member.

In the case of Frank and Jesse James, an extra five thousand dollars apiece was offered for conviction.

The most resolute of the officers on the trail of the outlaws was Sheriff James R. Timberlake of Clay County and Police Commissioner Henry Craig of Kansas City. Timberlake learned that Jesse and Frank were frequent visitors at the home of Charley and Robert Ford in Ray County. He devised a plan to keep an eye on them at the Harbison-Ford place. Disguised as a common laborer, he went into Ray County and spied on this residence for several weeks. It was his habit to hide at night next to the house, and in that way he learned a lot concerning the activities of Liddil and the Fords. His most important discovery was that these three men had a secret animosity toward Jesse James. He also learned about Wood Hite's murder.

Early in 1882 Sheriff Timberlake approached Martha Bolton with the suggestion that her brothers ought to see Governor Crittenden in connection with a plan to capture Jesse James. For their services, she was told, they would be given an unconditional pardon and ten thousand dollars of the fabulous reward money. Now the Fords had three reasons to betray Jesse: reward, revenge, fear. Through the common-law wife of Dick Liddil, Mattie Collins, Timberlake also urged Liddil to surrender to the authorities and give his assistance against Jesse James. The three men were finally persuaded.

When the newspapers printed conjectures about "the veiled woman" who had been to see Governor Crittenden at Jefferson City, nobody knew they were referring to Martha Bolton. It was with her that the governor completed the arrangements: the Fords were to be active in the capture, but Dick Liddil was to remain in the background, since Jesse was already suspicious of him.

Soon after Martha's interview with the governor, Jesse again called on the Ford brothers at the Harbison place and explained his plans for another robbery. Liddil was not present, for he had skipped to Kentucky, waiting for news from Mattie Collins about the governor's decision. He returned to Kansas City as soon as things were clear, and surrendered to Commissioner Craig. Shortly afterward he accompanied Sheriff Timberlake back to Kentucky in order to assist in the arrest of Clarence Hite. This boy was brought back to Missouri in February, 1882, and sentenced to twenty-five years in the state penitentiary for his complicity in several train robberies.

On February 22, Bob Ford had a secret meeting with Governor Crittenden at the St. James Hotel in Kansas City. He then joined Jesse as a new recruit for a bank robbery at Platte City. This robbery was planned for April 4. The route was laid out, and the time schedule was agreed upon. This information was quickly relayed to Sheriff Timberlake, who planned an ambush along the way.

The night of March 15 Charley and Bob Ford spent at the Samuel residence. Charley later said he had expected to kill Jesse that night, but the outlaw chief slept so lightly, with a gun in his hand, that he hesitated. The next day Charley went to the home of his sister, Martha Bolton, while Jesse went on to Kearney. There he met Bob Ford and returned to the Samuels' residence with him. On March 31, Charley Ford went to Jesse's home in St. Joseph, Missouri, where his brother Bob was staying for a few days.

Late on the night of April 1, Jesse rode up to the house of Elias Ford and called Bob outside. He told him he had work for him, and the two rode away together. The next day Elias Ford notified Sheriff Timberlake that Bob had gone to St. Joseph, no doubt in order to make the final preparations for the Platte City holdup. The sheriff notified his posse to be ready at a moment's notice and kept an engine steamed up so that they could race to St. Joseph.

EARLY MORNING

———◆———

April 3, 1882

Chapter 19

There was so damn little you could say to a woman.

You go over and over the same things. You think she understands, but she's just getting steam up to start over again.

Jesse stared through the bedroom window into the yard behind the house. The horses in the stable neighed, and somewhere a rooster crowed. He turned and looked back at the bed.

Zee was facing the opposite wall. She had the patchwork quilt pulled up to her neck, and her shoulders trembled under it with her quiet remorse.

Damn, Jesse thought. What can you do? She knew what it was going to be like when she married me. He reached up and scratched the back of his neck. He reasoned that Zee was acting strangely because she was pregnant again. It's the way of a woman, he said to himself. They don't care so much for themselves, but then they think about the children and the future. There always has to be a future, and I guess if you're carrying the future inside your body you can't think about anything else.

He reached for a shirt and slipped his arms into the sleeves. He left the room buttoning the shirt, closed the door quietly behind him, and entered the kitchen.

Stuffing the shirt into his trousers, he went to the cold stove. He shook the grate down, then removed the plates from the firebox. He crumpled paper and stuffed it inside, then he covered this with kindling, and put a match to the paper. He replaced the iron plates, opened the damper, and nudged the draft open with his foot. He waited until the fire was crackling, then he took the water bucket and went out through the back door.

Zee listened to the sounds in the kitchen. They were familiar and comforting to her, and for a moment she tried to for-

121

get the fear that plagued her. She knew that it might have something to do with her condition, but she also knew that it was more than that.

Jesse had changed. In the beginning he had been like some hero still carrying on the fight against the Yankees, but gradually he had grown more and more within himself. An example was the bad feeling between him and Frank. He even acted as though Frank were against him because he wanted to spend time with Annie.

Zee heard Jesse leave the kitchen through the back door, then she heard the sounds of the Fords. They were talking, but she could not hear the words.

She did not like the Fords, either one of them. With all the others who had ridden with Jesse and Frank she had a feeling that they had a purpose for what they were doing. But the ones who came now, like the Fords, made her feel uneasy.

"He went outside," Bob Ford whispered.

"I got ears," Charley said, his voice muffled by the covers.

"What's he up to?" Bob whispered.

"Damn it, Bob, cut it out. You're making me nervous."

Bob Ford slipped from the bed. He went to the window and pulled the shade aside to look out. He saw Jesse go to the pump and hang the bucket. He dropped the shade, and stood quietly, listening to the grating sounds of the pump handle and the spasmodic rush of water.

"You satisfied," Charley said. "He's getting water."

Bob came to the bed and leaned over. He grated his words through his teeth. "I tell you something's wrong," he said. "He knows we've got something planned."

"Let's call it off then," Charley said.

"That would make it worse. Damn it, Charley, I'm scared."

"Hell, boy," Charley said, "it was your idea. Stop worrying about it. The time comes, we just stay on our guard, that's all."

"He's wearing his gun out there," Bob hissed. "Why does he put on a gun to go pump water?"

"He's careful," Charley said.

"Him and them guns," Bob said. "He don't do nothing without them guns."

Jesse finished pumping. He lifted the bucket from the pump and placed it on the ground. He stood and stretched, looking about him at the sun streaming across the yard.

It might be nice to leave the road, he thought, but it never really worked. He had tried it down in Nashville, and he had finally gotten bored with it. He knew that he had become more brooding, but he had more on his mind. It wasn't the same since Northfield. Perhaps after this Platte City job he would try it again. He owed it to Zee.

Lifting the bucket he walked back to the house and entered the kitchen. He filled the large kettle and put it on the stove.

The house was coming to life. He could hear the children talking together, and the sounds of Zee dressing, and one of the Fords putting on his boots. He left the kitchen again and went to the barn.

The horses stirred in their stalls when he entered the dim interior. He pushed the door back to let the light flood in. He talked to the horses while he filled the nose bags and slipped them over their heads. He brought water from the pump, then pulled down fresh hay.

Sitting on an upturned keg, he brought out his pipe and tobacco.

I'd feel better if Frank was riding with me, he thought. First thing I gotta do after this job is make it up with Frank. It was harder and harder to find good men these days.

Striking a large sulfur match, he held it to the pipe and puffed hard. The smoke sifted through the rays of sunlight and drifted away.

He heard the back door open and close. Shifting slightly, he could see Bob and Charley Ford walk to the pump with their towels.

In the past week he had had to keep reassuring himself that Bob and Charley would work out. There was a time when he wouldn't have let Bob Ford hold the horses. The boy was too nervous and needed a tight rein. Charley had been a pretty good man, but lately he was also on edge.

Getting up from the keg, he left the barn and walked to the pump. Charley was working the handle and Bob was doubled over, splashing water on his face.

"Morning," Jesse said.

"Morning," Charley said, "good weather to ride."

"Hope it holds," Jesse said.

"Horses look alright?"

"Fine," Jesse said. "They're good animals."

Bob came up sputtering and reached for his towel. He

dried his face, then took the pump handle while Charley washed.

"Nice day for a Monday," Bob said. "I always hate Mondays."

"Well, it's sure a bright one," Jesse said. He turned away and walked back to the barn to remove the nose bags from the horses.

"You see what he did?" Bob whispered urgently.

"What?" Charley sputtered.

"He walked right away from me."

"He's feeding the horses," Charley said. "Dammit, boy, get a grip on yourself!"

"I tell you he knows."

"Shut up and hand me the towel."

When Jesse came out of the barn he closed the door after him. The Fords had gone back into the house. He stood for a moment looking about him, then walked to the house. Although the house—at Thirteenth and Lafayette Streets—stood by itself on a hill, he was used to being wary of prying eyes. He was wearing his hip gun and it was always best to keep it covered with a coat.

Zee was standing at the stove when he entered the kitchen.

"You feel better?" he asked.

She nodded. "I'm sorry I acted up," she said.

He smiled and touched her arm. "I'm gonna go down for the papers," he said.

"Don't take too long. I'll have breakfast when you get back."

Bob and Charley came into the kitchen from the bedroom. They were both dressed.

"I'm going down for the papers, Bob," Jesse said. "Come along."

"I think I'll stay here," Bob said.

There was a time to assert authority, and Jesse seized the opportunity. He had to show Bob that a suggestion from him was an order. During a bank job it could mean the difference between success and failure. "I'd rather you come," he said.

Bob's eyes flicked from Jesse to Charley. His hand went up and he plucked nervously at his thin mustache. "Very well," he said.

Jesse went into the living room and slipped on his coat. Bob followed him and they left the house together.

They walked down the long hill in silence. At the cigar store Bob said he would wait outside. Jesse went in. The newspapers were on the counter. The headline on the Kansas City *Times* caught his eyes, and he stopped to read it. He pursed his lips and scowled thoughtfully.

"Morning, Mr. Howard," the clerk said.

"Morning."

"Looks like spring is here for sure," the clerk said.

Jesse nodded, but his mind was occupied. He picked up the *Times*, the St. Louis *Republican*, and the Kansas City *Journal*. He paid the clerk, folded the papers under his arm and left the store.

Bob fell in beside him, and they walked together up the hill.

"You hear any news about Liddil while you was in Kansas City?" Jesse asked.

Bob tensed, but he answered, "Nope."

They went the rest of the way in silence until they reached the house. They went into the kitchen.

Charley was seated at the table with a cup of coffee before him. Zee had ham frying on the stove and she was breaking eggs into a pan.

"I'll have your coffee in a second," she said.

"Any interesting news?" Charley asked.

Jesse dropped the papers on the table. The *Times* was on the top and the usually sedate front page was now emblazoned with a black headline announcing the arrest of Dick Liddil.

Bob's gasp of surprise was audible. He stared at the headline, recalling Jesse's question. There was no doubt of it now. He was suspicious. Bob's fingers curled over the back of his chair and his knuckles were white under the pressure.

Shoot! his mind screamed. Draw now, and kill him. He was afraid. He could not make his muscles obey his mind. He watched Jesse go to his chair, pull it back, and sit down.

"Sit down, Bob," Jesse said.

He's just playing with me, Bob thought. He's just waiting for the right moment. I'll be careful. I'll watch.

Pulling his own chair back, Bob sat down. He leaned back to allow Zee to fill his coffee cup.

Jesse was puzzled by Bob Ford's reaction to the headline. He was frightened, Jesse knew, but he wasn't quite sure of the connection. He reached out and lifted the paper, his eyes scanning the story.

Zee brought the first eggs and ham and placed the platter on the table. The children were in the back yard, their squeals and laughter sharp in the kitchen silence.

Jesse shook the paper and cleared his throat. He looked across at Bob. "You told me you didn't know anything new about Dick," he said.

"I didn't," Bob answered.

Charley was cutting his ham. He stopped and glanced at Jesse. "What about Dick?"

Jesse turned the headline toward Charley. "He surrendered three weeks ago, it says here," Jesse said. He looked back at Bob. "You were right there in the neighborhood."

"I didn't hear anything about it," Bob said. He was fidgeting and biting his lip.

"That's mighty strange," Jesse said.

"They were probably keeping it quiet," Charley said. "You never know what the damn law is going to do."

"Well, never mind, Bob," Jesse said, folding the paper and putting it aside. "It doesn't really matter." He took up his knife and fork and reached for the eggs.

He knows! Bob's mind wailed with the terror of a man caged with disaster. He sat in the chair stiffly, the breath constricting his chest, his heart beating wildly. His fingers gripped the edge of the table.

He stared at Jesse who was hunched over his plate, eating and glancing sideways at the newspaper.

Shoot! Draw and shoot! Get it over with now! The thoughts assailed him, but he could not bring himself to reach down and touch the gun riding his hip.

Damn, why didn't I think about the newspapers. Timberlake warned me that the reporters might find out about Liddil.

The injustice of it nagged at him and he felt like crying out in anger. One little mistake! Everything was going just right. One mistake!

"Eat, Bob," Jesse said, looking up and smiling across the table.

"I—I'm not hungry," Bob said.

"Better eat, Boy," Jesse said. "We got a hard ride tonight."

Why doesn't he leave me alone? He's trying to ride me into a showdown. Well, I won't let him. I'll stay alive. I've worked too hard for tonight. Look at him smile at me, playing with me. He thinks I don't know what he has in mind. I know, I damn well know. He figures he'll kill me on the road tonight.

The sudden thought brought up a well of panic and he began to tremble.

Charley was having trouble chewing the ham. He tried to keep his eyes on the plate, but they kept straying to his brother.

Christ almighty, the kid is going to pieces. That newspaper threw him. It was a bad break and Jesse is no fool, but he better pull himself together and bluff it through.

"Why don't you go into the other room, Bob," Charley said. "You don't look so good."

"I reckon I'm off my feed," Bob said.

Okay, okay, Charley thought. I gave you an out, now get the hell out of here and pull yourself together.

The kitchen of the farmhouse in Kearney was cold and Zerelda Samuel shuddered. Favoring the arm that had been shattered by the Pinkerton's bomb, she reached for wood from the side of the stove and chunked it into the firebox.

She was troubled by the split-up of Frank and Jesse, and it was constantly on her mind. I better write to Mister Frank, she said to herself. The young'un needs him. Yessir, I'll write today. Maybe if I talk to Jesse I can pound some sense into his head. It ain't right for them two boys to be unfriendly.

Frank sat on the edge of the bed. His cough had abated, and he was regaining his breath. His mind was a turmoil of thoughts. Mostly he thought about whether he could really leave the road and make it stick.

What will I do when Jesse shows up and asks me to ride again? I know I don't want to. In the end we've got to get killed. We've been at it too long.

Time has passed us by, he thought. We're antiques. We try to make ourselves think we're still fighting the war, but it doesn't stick anymore.

No, I can't ride again. When Jesse comes I'll just have to keep my head.

Zee brought more coffee to the table and filled Jesse's cup. Charley refused.

"You haven't touched a thing, Bob," she said.

Why is he so frightened? There's something wrong. I can feel it myself. She looked at Jesse, but his face told her nothing.

The kitchen door slammed and little Jesse bolted into the room. She whirled.

"Mama!" the boy cried.

She grasped his arm and turned him back to the door. "You play outside with your sister until the men are finished breakfast."

"She's eating dirt," the boy said.

"Well, stop her, for heaven's sake." She pushed the boy through the door and stood a moment with her hands on her hips. She turned and went back to the stove.

Bob pushed back from the table and stood. "I—uh, pardon me," he said.

He turned abruptly and walked across the kitchen. He entered the living room. He felt safe for a moment, but then he heard a chair scrape and he knew instinctively that it was Jesse.

Crossing the room, he stood by the window. He heard Jesse come into the room.

His heart thudded against his ribs. He had to fight to control his breathing. His hands itched for the comforting feel of his gun butt; he dared not move his fingers toward the gun.

"This job has got you nervous, Bob," Jesse said behind him.

"I reckon so," he answered.

Why doesn't he just come out with it? What's he trying to prove?

Turn, his mind shouted. Turn and draw. You'll have the edge. He could not move. It was not because he was a coward. He had fought other men. But he was an untried boy and the man behind him was a legend. He was waiting for Jesse James to put a bullet in his back and he could not make a move. A cold sweat prickled his body.

"Just take it easy, Boy. This time tomorrow you'll be in action," Jesse said.

Bob turned slowly. He's not going to kill me here, he thought with a flood of relief. Of course not. He wouldn't do it in front of his wife and kids.

Jesse was standing in the middle of the room. He was smiling with good humor.

He's gonna do it tonight, Bob thought. On the way to Platte City he'll drop me. I gotta get out of here. We got to call this off. I'll say I'm sick. Anything, but I gotta get out of this. I'm not a match for him, and he knows it. The panic was riding him, and he forced his legs to move. He crossed to a chair and sat down, his body rigid with fear.

"Warm in here," Jesse said.

Bob clasped his hands to keep them from trembling. He watched Jesse cross the room and open the window. Jesse started to take off his coat, then stopped. "Wouldn't want any folks passing by and seeing me in here with all this hardware," he said, chuckling. "They might think there was a bad man in here." He started to draw the curtains, then stopped. "Shame to keep a morning like this out," he said.

Bob could not answer. It seemed to him that Jesse was acting out a charade. He did not know for what reason, but his panic was growing by the minute. He watched with disbelief as Jesse removed his coat, then unbuckled the holster at his waist, and dropped it on the couch. Jesse then removed his hide-out gun and put it down.

Bob caught his breath. He had never seen Jesse unarmed before. His stomach muscles tensed. There had to be another gun. He was just making a show of being disarmed so Bob would make a play. Bob was also goaded into anger by the thought that Jesse found him too insignificant to be concerned about.

He watched Jesse turn and gaze at a picture on the wall. It was a print of the death of Stonewall Jackson.

"That picture's awful dusty," Jesse said.

Strange last words for the most notorious outlaw in the history of America. A moment of destiny. In that moment the world continued to turn on its axis. Somewhere a baby was born. Somewhere a man or woman ceased to breathe. Somewhere a man crossed the street on his way to work. Somewhere something happened to millions of people, each in his own life, his own sphere.

In St. Joseph, Missouri, a man took a feather duster from a table, pulled a straight-backed chair across the room to the wall, and climbed upon it. He faced a framed picture, flicked the duster across it, then reached up to straighten it.

Bob Ford bit into his lower lip until he tasted blood. He reached down and slipped his gun into his hand. He stared at it a moment. The silver plate glittered. It had been a gift from Jesse James, a .44 revolver. He pressed his back into the chair. His arm came up and he gripped the gun in both hands. He took a deep breath and thumbed back the hammer.

The three clicks were loud in the silent room. The man on the chair turned away from the wall. It was a stern, black-bearded man, now staring in disbelief.

Bob Ford saw the face in close-up. He pulled the trigger.

The explosion reverberated through the small frame house. A scream echoed from the kitchen. A chair toppled over.

Bob stared at the figure standing above him. He saw the small black hole in the forehead. The room was scented with burned cordite. The figure did not move. It was true the legend could not be killed. He held his breath, his muscles were frozen. He could not pull the trigger again.

Jesse twisted slowly. The chair rocked. His body crashed to the floor.

Bob still did not move.

Charley rushed into the room. He stopped and stared at the body, then at his brother. Zee was in the doorway. She looked at Jesse, then at Bob.

"You killed him," she screamed. She buried her face in her hands and wailed, then she ran forward and dropped to her knees, lifting the body in her arms.

The tension snapped, and Bob vaulted from the chair. He ran from the house. The tight constriction of fear had been lifted from him, and he ran down the hill shouting like a man delivered to the gods.

The news went through St. Joseph like an electric current, the news that would be flashed to every continent on the globe.

Jesse James was dead!

THE INQUEST

Chapter 20

On the morning of the murder, at ten o'clock, Assistant Coroner Heddens was notified, and he instructed Undertaker Sidenfaden to remove Jesse's remains to his establishment. As the body lay in a remote room of the building, reporters compared photographs of Jesse James with the dead man's features and searched for identifying scars. They found two large bullet wounds in the right side of the breast, within three inches of the nipple; a bullet wound in the leg, and the top of the middle finger on the left hand had been cut off. Another identifying sign was a birthmark on the back of Jesse's right arm above the elbow: a dark brown spot in the shape of a potato. Besides, they saw the result of Jesse's getting his left foot caught in the stirrup and dislocating an inside anklebone which had never healed properly but was pushed inward. (Was this ankle injured at the Gallatin bank robbery?) There was another mark that most people knew nothing about: during his boyhood in 1862 an abscess in his right groin had been lanced by Dr. Glen E. Bishop of St. Joseph.

Telegrams had been sent to Governor Crittenden, Sheriff Timberlake and Commissioner Craig. The Fords both surrendered to Marshal Craig of St. Joseph, and they were placed in jail.

Corydon F. Craig, the marshal's young son, took a fancy to the Fords, and he saw to it that they were furnished with cigarettes and various good things to eat during their brief stay in jail. After their release, Bob Ford presented young Craig with the gun he had used to kill Jesse James, as a token of his appreciation. Although many have claimed it was a Colt .45 caliber, improved pattern, it was not. It was a Smith & Wesson No. 3, New Model, nickel-plated, 6½-inch barrel, .44 caliber, Serial No. 3766, according to the inquest testimony given by the Ford brothers.

At the turn of the century Craig was in Baltimore where he called at the office of James E. Gary, postmaster general under President McKinley. Craig asked for a small loan, offering as security the "gun which killed Jesse James." Of course, it was then not too many years after James' death and not much value was attached to the weapon. Consequently Gary refused the loan. However, E. Stanley Gary, son of James Gary, shared his father's office and, though he, too, refused to accept the gun as security on a loan, he bought it from Craig. In Springfield, Massachusetts, young Gary had Smith & Wesson engrave it: "Bob Ford killed Jesse James with this revolver at St. Joseph, Mo., 1882." Gary often refused handsome cash offers for the gun. A sworn affidavit by Corydon Craig is in the possession of Henry G. Lingenfelder of Baltimore, the present owner of it.

Bob Ford's talk to newspapermen before the inquest differs somewhat from his personal report to the governor, in which he stated he was alone in the room when Jesse was shot. Possibly he changed his story so that Charley Ford could share in the reward—blood money which they never collected.

So they say the dead man isn't Jesse James, do they? Then they are mistaken. I first met Jesse James three years ago, and I have made no mistake. He used to come over to the house when I was on my oldest brother's farm. Last November he moved here to St. Joe and went under the name of Thomas Howard. He rented a house on a hill, back of the Worlds Hotel, a quiet part of the town and not thickly settled. My brother Charley and I had known nearly all of the gang, but had never worked with them otherwise.

I was in collusion with the detectives, and was one of the party that went to Kentucky and arrested Clarence Hite last February. Hite got twenty-five years in the penitentiary. Jesse never suspected that we were false to him, and as his gang was all broken up, he wanted new material and regarded us favorably.

Today his wife, and a boy of seven, and a girl of three, were in the kitchen. Jesse was in the front sitting room, where he slept. Never knew him to be so careless. He commenced brushing the dust off some pictures, but first took off his weapons and laid them on the bed. There was a Colt's revolver and a Smith & Wesson, each

.45 caliber. He also had in the room a Winchester repeating rifle, and a breech-loading shotgun.

As he turned from the bed, we stepped between him and his guns and pulled on him. He turned his head like lightning. I fired. The ball hit him over the left eye and coming out behind the right ear. Charley had his finger on the trigger, but he saw that he was done for and did not shoot. Not one of us spoke a word. He fell dead at Charley's feet. We then got our hats, went to the telegraph office and sent several wires.

The inquest began at three o'clock that afternoon in the Circuit Court Room of the courthouse. Mrs. James arrived in the custody of Marshal Craig. The two Fords had been kept in separate rooms until the jury announced they were ready to hear the testimony. Then they entered the court. Since their arrest was merely a formality, and since they claimed to be afraid of an attack by the public, they had asked permission to keep their guns even though they were in custody. Therefore they were heavily armed when they appeared.

Charley Ford was the first witness to be called to the stand.

My home is about two miles from Richmond, Missouri, where I have resided for the past three years. I left home on the third day of November last at the request of Jesse James, who was then a resident of Kansas City. He removed to St. Joseph on the fifth, and I accompanied him. After moving to St. Joe Jesse said he wanted to take a trip through Kansas to see how the banks were situated, and said he would get the men. He wanted to know if I knew anybody who would help us. I told him I thought I could get my brother to help us if I could go down and see him. We went to his mother's in Clay County and stayed until Friday night, and then to my brother's and stayed until Saturday, when we left for this city. On the way up Jesse said there was going to be a murder trial at Platte City and we would go over there, and if everything was all right we would rob the bank. He said when they were making the speeches everybody would be in the courthouse, and we would rob the bank. This morning we had come from the barn, where we had been feeding and currying the horses, and Jesse complained of being warm. He pulled off his coat and threw it on the bed, and said he would take off his belt, as somebody might see it. Then he got up on a chair to brush off some pictures, and when he turned his back I gave my brother the wink to shoot Jesse; I intended to fire also, but Bob was a little quicker than I, and fired first. I had my finger on the trigger, and was just going to fire, but I saw his shot was a death shot, and did not fire. He heard us cock our pistols and began to turn his head. The ball struck him in the head and he fell. We then went to the telegraph office and sent dispatches to Craig and Timberlake. After that we went to the marshal's office, where a policeman told us that the marshal had gone down in the direction of the house. We went down and gave ourselves up. We killed him because Governor Crittenden said he would like to have him captured, and that he would give $10,000 reward to break up the band of outlaws.

Jesse came to my house two years ago last summer. He was a sporting man and so was I. He gambled and drank a little, and so did I. I was acquainted with Miller, and Miller came in and introduced him as Mr. Jackson. He stayed until the next day, when he left, and after that Miller told me it was Jesse James.

I did not see him any more for a long time. When I did see him I asked him where Miller was, and he said Miller was in bad health and he did not think he could live long. He was there two or three times last summer and once last fall, and asked me to go with him and rob banks and trains. I never robbed anything with him. My brother and I had made it up to kill him. I went to see my brother two weeks ago last Thursday night at my uncle's, Bill Ford. He had left Kansas City with the intention of making up a party and watching the house so that if Jesse came around they could get him. But the weather got bad and they gave it up, and I went to see then to White Cloud, Kansas. He said he liked the bank Hiawatha, then to Pawnee City, next to Forrest City, my brother and told him what I wanted.

We went to Nebraska together. We went first to in Forrest City, and said he wanted to take that bank, but I told him I did not want to go into that, as I was sick. We then came up to Oregon. He said he wanted to look at the bank. We then returned here. He would go into the bank and get a bill changed, and while there would take a look and see whether they were caged up, what sort of a looking man it was, and whether they had a time lock on. We never traveled on the cars. Jesse said he preferred to travel on horseback because he couldn't stop at the small villages when on the cars. We spent the daytime in the house since coming here. At night we would walk uptown and get the papers. He generally took the Kansas City papers and the *Police News*. Jesse sometimes walked out east of town, during the day. He had a good deal of money—some $1,500—but I don't know where he kept it. I had no expenses and used no money. My brother and I had planned the killing of Jesse. We were to get behind him if we could get him to lay his pistols off. This morning I gave my brother the wink. He had a Smith & Wesson and could get it out quicker than I could mine. I knew that it was nonsense to try to take him, for he said he would not surrender to a hundred men, and if three men should step out in front of him and shoot him he would kill them all before he fell. When shot he was about four feet from me. He fell on his face.

Robert Ford was then called to the stand. As he walked forward he was the center of all eyes in the room. It was hardly believable that this boyish-looking, slender young man could have killed Jesse James. His sunken hazel eyes, large and restless, flitted around the courtroom as he took the stand. His evidence was given in a clear, loud voice, without a catch or a tremor.

My name is Robert Ford and I am twenty-one years of age. My residence for the past three or four years has been in Ray County, Missouri, near the town of Richmond. In January last I had a conversation with Governor Crittenden, the result of which I became a detective to hunt the James outlaws. My first meeting with Jesse James occurred about three years ago, when in company with Ed Miller he stopped at my house over night and discussed the robbing of a railroad train; the members of his gang at that time were Dick Liddil, Wood Hite, Ed Miller, Clarence Hite, and Jim Cummins; I never met any of these except Ed Miller, Jim Cummins, and Wood

Hite. Governor Crittenden asked me if I thought I could catch Jesse James, and I answered yes, and at this same interview I besought the governor to pardon Dick Liddil, and agreed to undertake the arrest of Jesse. The governor therefore agreed to pay $10,000 apiece for the production of Jesse and Frank James, whether dead or alive. This interview occurred at St. James Hotel in Kansas City.

I have been with Jesse constantly since last Sunday night, but Charley has been watching for an opportunity to capture him since last November. I was with Jesse about ten days, when at his request I accompanied him to his mother's home and slept with him in the barn. We remained there for two days, then started on horseback for St. Joseph, stopping over night in a church, and before reaching the town we hid in a patch of timber until night, so as to make our entrance unobserved. That was one week ago last night. I rode a horse that had been stolen from a man named Robinson, of Clay County. Jesse and I had a talk yesterday about robbing the bank at Platte City, at which Charley and I both agreed to assist. Between eight and nine o'clock this morning, while the three of us were in a room in Jesse's house, Jesse pulled off his coat and also his pistols, two of which he constantly wore, and then got up onto a chair for the purpose of brushing off a picture. While Jesse was thus engaged Charley winked at me, so that I knew he meant for me to shoot; so, as quickly as possible, I drew my pistol and aiming at Jesse's head, which was not more than four feet from the muzzle of my weapon, I fired, and Jesse tumbled headlong from the chair on which he was standing and fell on his face. Just before the killing Jesse and Charley had been currying the horses; I did not go out of the house because Jesse said it was better that I should not be seen about the house. I usually remained all day indoors, but after night I generally went down into the city to purchase papers. After the shooting I told Mrs. James it was accidental, but she would not believe me. I went directly from Jesse's house to the telegraph station and sent a dispatch to Governor Crittenden, informing him of what I had done. I have heard him frequently declare he would never be taken alive.

This closed the testimony on Monday, and court was adjourned to meet the next morning at ten. Before that hour arrived, the courtroom was filled by people anxious to get a glimpse of Jesse's mother, Mrs. Samuel, and his widow. Prior to going to the courthouse Mrs. Samuel and Zee James went to the Sidenfaden funeral parlor to view the remains. Mrs. Samuel almost swooned as she cried, "My poor boy! My dear son! My darling boy!"

When asked if the remains were those of her son, Mrs. Samuel replied, "Yes, it is Jesse, all right. Would to God it was not!"

There was considerable excitement all over St. Joseph as well as in Kansas City. Not since the assassination of President Garfield had the people been so concerned at the death of one man. Many persons in St. Joe scoffed at the thought of its being Jesse James and declared it was a "put-up job" to obtain the reward money. But it was Jesse, all right. An impressive list of identifiers made sure of that: Prosecuting Attorney Wallace, Harrison Trow, James Wilkerson, J. Clay, Mattie Collins, Mr. Mimmbs (or Mimms), Rev. William James, C. D. Axman, Lamartine Hudspeth (a long-time friend of the outlaw and a close relative), Ben Morrow and Sim Whitsett (who had served with Jesse under William Clarke Quantrill). Many times these last-named men had given assistance to Jesse when he was on the run. They made no bones about it, either; in fact, they were rather proud of the help they had rendered him.

After an intermission, Mrs. Samuel entered the courtroom, and then the inquest continued. Henry H. Craig, Kansas City Police Commissioner, was called to the stand, and he made this brief statement:

> I was not acquainted with Jesse James personally, but am positive the body of the dead man is the outlaw, as it corresponds with the description I have heard. I know Robert Ford, and for two months he has assisted Sheriff Timberlake and myself in the endeavor to capture Jesse James. He was not employed regularly by us, but acted in good faith, and according to our instructions, and assisted in every way he could to aid us. Charley Ford I had never seen until I came to St. Joe, but understand he and Robert had some understanding.

Sheriff Timberlake was next called and gave an interesting little account.

Was acquainted with Jesse James during life and recognize the body as that of Jesse. Had known him since 1864, and saw him last time in 1870. Knew his face as well as anyone. He had the second joint of his third finger shot off by which I also recognize him. Ford was acting under my instructions and said if he could see Charley Ford we could accomplish our end the sooner, and he acted squarely to all agreements.

There is a lot of misthinking about what the governor had to do with Jesse's demise. He has been misrepresented in this matter of the killing of Jesse James. He did not know where James was living, nor did I until after he was killed. Now let me tell you something else you did not know. Jesse James knew Bob Ford's mission, and he was only waiting for a chance to kill him. Bob knew that Jesse suspected him, and that it was a question between them who fell first. When I placed Bob Ford where Jesse picked him up, I said, "Bob, Jesse knows that you have been with me as well as I do. He will kill you if he gets the chance." He said to me, "Yes, I know." I then said, "Capture him if you can when he first comes to meet you. If you can't do it, then wait for your chance. Don't allow yourself to be found alone with him." At that time Charley Ford was a genuine friend and companion of Jesse. He never went into the scheme to take Jesse until Bob talked to him. I knew within three hours after the time that Jesse and Charley came along and took up Bob. I had no idea where they had gone. For ten days I suffered mental agony, expecting any hour to hear that Bob was dead, and when I at last did hear of the killing, and how it was done, I knew in a minute that Jesse had only taken his revolvers off in the presence of Bob to make him believe that he stood solid. He never dreamed that the drop would be taken upon him then. That very night, on the ride toward Platte City, which had been seemingly agreed upon, Jesse would have shot Bob Ford through the head.

Dick Liddil was next called to the witness stand. He said:

I have seen the body of the dead man and recognize it; I was with him a good deal last summer and know him perfectly, I also recognize him from the wounds on the hand and on the right side.

Charles Alderman, who operated a livery stable in St. Joseph, had this to say:

Am a trader; was not acquainted with Jesse James in life; have seen the body and recognize it as that of a man I traded horses with but did not know who he was; and last Saturday I got it back from Charles Ford, who had been at my place several times. He said he wanted a horse for his uncle, who I now presume is Jesse James.

This statement led many people to believe that the Ford brothers were related to Jesse James, but Alderman had merely meant to show that when Charles Ford spoke of an uncle he had in mind Jesse James, who had sent him to get a horse. While living at St. Joseph with Jesse, both Bob and Charley had used the name of Johnson, claiming to be nephews of Thomas Howard of 1318 Lafayette Street.

The next statement was made by Deputy Marshal Finley of St. Joseph:

I was not acquainted with Jesse James; went to the house where he was killed in answer to a telephone where the man was killed; found him on his back, and from Mrs. James got a description of the two men who killed the man, and started out in search of them. She said one was her nephew and the other young man, both named Johnson, but no relation. As we were going out, we met the boys coming back. Bob said he was the man who killed the person in the house. We could not find them at first, but did find a necktie and a gold ring with the name of Jesse James on the inside. Afterwards we found two watches in the trunk. There was some small change in an old pocketbook, which I gave to Mrs. James. On a one dollar gold piece as a scarf pin were the initials "J.W.J." Most of the property is now in the hands of the city marshal.

The name of Mrs. Zerelda Samuel, the mother of the dead

outlaw, was called, and every man in the courtroom stretched his neck to get a good look at her. With her head erect and with a proud air, Mrs. Samuel passed up the center aisle, accompanied by Mrs. Turner, a friend, as well as by the widow and children of Jesse James.

Coroner Heddens asked Mrs. Samuel if the body was that of her son Jesse.

> Yes, it is Jesse, all right. I live in Clay County, and am the mother of Jesse James. I have seen the body since my arrival and have recognized it as that of my son, Jesse; the lady at my side is my daughter-in-law and the children are hers. He was a kind husband and son.

Here she broke down and moaned several times, "Oh, my poor boy."

The coroner's jury returned the following verdict after less than an hour's deliberation.

STATE OF MISSOURI) SS
COUNTY OF BUCHANAN)

An inquisition taken at St. Joseph, in the County of Buchanan, on the third day of April, 1882, before me, James W. Heddens, M.D., coroner of the County aforesaid, upon their review of the body of Jesse W. James, then and there lying dead, S. H. Sommers, W. H. Chouning, J. W. Moore, Thomas Norris, William Turner, W. H. George, good and lawful householders in the township of Washington, who, being duly sworn and charged diligently to enquire and true presentment make, how and in what manner, and by whom the said Jesse W. James came to his death, upon their oaths do say:

That the body of the deceased is that of Jesse W. James and that he came to his death by a wound in the head, caused by a pistol shot fired intentionally by the hand of Robert Ford, in witness whereof as well the jurors aforesaid, have to this inquisition put their names at the place and on the day aforesaid.

Right after the inquest the two Ford boys were committed to the St. Joseph jail, charged with the murder of Jesse W. James, on a warrant sworn out by Mrs. Jesse James.

The news, when it was received in Kansas City, created a sensation, although at first the report was treated with incredulity. Even late on the afternoon of April 3 unbelievers could be found. That afternoon Police Commissioner Craig left for St. Joseph with a heavily armed posse to guard the body of Jesse James and to give protection to the man who had committed the murder. At the police station it was learned that Bob Ford, a young man who had been hanging around the station for several weeks past, was the person who had shot Jesse James. From the police it was now for the first time learned that Ford was under the control of Craig and had been used as an instrument of the law.

There was a dispute between the St. Joseph authorities and Sheriff Timberlake and Commissioner Craig regarding the disposition of the outlaw's remains. On April 5 Governor Crittenden received the following telegram from Sheriff Timberlake, who was at St. Joseph:

> What must I do? The officers won't either turn over the body of Jesse to his wife or his arms to me.

In reply the governor wired O. M. Spencer, prosecuting attorney of Buchanan County, at St. Joseph:

> Just informed your officers will not turn the body of James over to his wife nor deliver his arms to me. I hope you will have done both. Humanity suggests the one, and a preservation of such relics for the state the other. His jewelry should be held for the present. One paper says he had on my lost watch.

The governor placed little credit in the report that his fine watch stolen fifteen years earlier was found in the possession of Jesse James. There had been a newspaper hoax to the effect that the outlaw had told the governor he could have his watch back if he went after it and identified it; but that was an imaginary incident.

Finally the body was turned over to the sheriff with the agreement that it should be buried in the front yard of the old James homestead at Kearney.

AFTERMATH

Chapter 21

On the evening of April 5, when the eastbound train stopped at St. Joseph, the Jesse James funeral cortege was in charge of Marshal Craig. At six o'clock a carriage drove up to the station. Mrs. Samuel stepped out and, leaning on the arm of an officer, walked to the train. She insisted on inspecting the baggage car to see for herself that Jesse's body had been placed on board. Members of the mourning family were, besides Mrs. Samuel, Mrs. Zee James, the two James children, L. W. James (Jesse's cousin), and R. T. Mimmbs (brother of Jesse's widow).

At the depot a man tried to shoot Mrs. Samuel, but he was disarmed and thrown into the street. No official record has been kept of this attack nor of the assailant's name.

At nine that evening the train reached Cameron, Missouri, where a special train was to take the party on to Kearney. However, the special train failed to arrive, and at midnight Marshal Craig had the coffin removed to the caboose of a freight train. He loaded the mourners on that, and they arrived in Kearney just before daylight on April 6. Jesse's remains were taken to the Kearney Hotel and again exposed to public view. Hundreds of people took the opportunity to gaze upon the lifeless form of the once notorious Jesse James.

At two o'clock that afternoon the casket, a metal vault of imitation rosewood engraved with the name "Jesse James," was placed in a wagon and started for the Mt. Olivet Baptist Church, followed by a large crowd. The wagon following the hearse contained Jesse's relatives, while the second wagon carried the pallbearers: Sheriff Timberlake, Deputy Sheriff Reed, Charles Scott, J. B. Henderson, J. D. Ford (the former mayor of Liberty, Missouri, and no relation to Bob and Charley Ford), Benjamin Flanders and James Vaughn.

Within an hour the procession reached the church, where Jesse's body was turned over to the pastor, J. M. P. Martin.

He officiated at the service, assisted by the Rev. R. H. Jones of Lathrop, Missouri. After the service the procession started toward the early home of the outlaw, four miles from town. It was hidden on the southern side by a gentle eminence and so could not be seen by the chance passer-by. Only the relatives were admitted to the premises, because the family insisted on quiet—Jesse's half-brother, John Samuel, was suffering from a wound he had recently received during a dance-hall brawl. The casket was taken into the house so that John might have a last look at Jesse's face. It is believed that a last look was taken at the same time by another brother, Frank.

At five o'clock the body was finally consigned to a very deep grave, dug opposite and near the kitchen, just inside a plank fence that separated the yard from a pasture and under a gigantic coffee bean tree. After the casket had been lowered, Mrs. Samuel screamed that someone had cut off Jesse's right hand. So determined was she that the men had to lift the casket and open it again, to assure her that she was mistaken. She calmed down somewhat after that.

On April 6, the Jefferson City *Republican* published an interview with Governor Crittenden:

> In an interview with Governor Crittenden today his excellency stated that neither Craig, Timberlake, nor himself were aware that Jesse James was residing at St. Joseph, but supposed he still lived in Kansas City, and that he was inclined to discredit the first telegram he received of the killing of James, because it came from St. Joseph, not believing he had gone there for any purpose. He now understands the reason James selected such a locality. It was to the bold outlaw a commanding position from which he could operate in Kansas and Missouri. "The house," said the governor, "was situated admirably for protection and escape, presenting means of concealment for his stolen plunder and himself, and a convenient stable in which he lodged his stolen horses. A good general always looks when preparing for battle as well for accessible means of retreat as of attack."
>
> The governor said, "The honest, good people of Missouri should stand by the Ford boys, and will, I verily believe, as soon as the excitement incident to the death of James has subsided. Why should anyone with a proper appreciation of honest citizenship aside from con-

sideration regarding his own mother and loving little family regret his death? If not killed when he was, he would have attacked the bank at Platte City, and in perpetrating the robbery would have killed in all probability some one or more officials in the ill-fated bank; then would have gone to Kansas, returned and attacked the bank at Forrest City and killed one or more of its officials.

"Should not these things be considered? Must we overlook not only his past but anticipated robberies and murders in the future and grieve over his deprivations? I say no, a thousand times no. I have no excuses to make, no apologies to render any living man for the part I played in this bloody drama, nor has Craig nor has Timberlake. The life of one honest law-abiding man however humble is worth more to society and a state than a legion of Jesse Jameses. One is a blessing, the other a living, breathing, putrid curse. I am no admirer of any of the acts of the outlaw. He may have occasionally done a good deed; if so, like the corsair, it was 'one virtue linked with a thousand crimes.'

"I am not regretful of his death, and have no words of censure for the boys who removed him. They deserve credit in my candid solemn opinion.

"When John U. Waring, one of the bloodiest murderers who ever disgraced Kentucky, was shot down in the streets of Versailles, in that state, in 1835, by a well-known man concealed in the upper room of the courthouse (and Waring was no worse than Jesse James), no legal examination was ever made in the case and no volumes of denunciations were ever heaped upon the murderer. All said he did a righteous act, as the victim was an outlaw, a *hostis humanis*. Why should these Ford boys be so abused? If they are guilty of a hideous sin against society, others are also equally guilty. Without fear or favor I say these boys did an act that will redound to the prosperity and advancement of Missouri and remove the great shadow that has hung too long over this great state. All honor to the brave officer who accomplished the work. If you want to know the value of the deed ask the managers of banks, ask the owners of land in that part of the state, ask the managers of the many railroads constructed in this state, ask the ticket agents at St. Louis, Kansas City, and Chicago, ask the hotel keepers at St. Louis and Kansas City, ask the property holders and real-estate agents in Kansas City and in Jackson County, ask those who own land in Clay and Platte, hear all of their responses and then say it was not a good deed in behalf of law, order, and general prosperity."

Many thousands read the governor's eloquent words and agreed with them. Many more thousands heard the remarks of Major John Newman Edwards, fire-eating adjutant of Confederate General Jo Shelby, and Governor Crittenden's political career was ruined forever. Edwards said:

Not one among all the hired cowards, hard on the hunt for blood money, dared face this wonderful outlaw, one even against twenty, until he had disarmed himself and turned his back on his assassins, the first and only time in a career which has passed from the realms of an almost fabulous romance into that of history.

We called him an outlaw, and he was; but fate made him so. When the war came he was just turned fifteen. The border was all aflame with steel and fire and ambuscade and slaughter. He flung himself into a band which had a black flag for a banner and devils for riders. What he did he did, and it was fearful. But it was war. It was Missouri against Kansas. It was Jim Lane and Jennison against Quantrill, Anderson, and Todd.

When the war closed Jesse James had no home. Proscribed, hunted, shot, driven away from among his people, a price put on his head, what else could he do, with such a nature, except what he did do? He had to live. It was his country. The graves of his kindred were there. He refused to be banished from his birthright, and when he was hunted he turned savagely about and hunted his hunters. Would to God he were alive today to make a righteous butchery of a few more of them.

There never was a more cowardly and unnecessary murder committed in all America than this murder of Jesse James. It was done for money. It was done that a few men might get all the money. He had been living in St. Joseph for months. The Fords were with him. He was in their toils, for they meant to betray him. He was in the heart of a large city. One word would have summoned 500 armed men for his capture or extermination. Not a single one of the attacking party need to have been hurt. If, when his house had been surrounded, he had refused to surrender, he could have been killed on the inside of it and at long range. The chances for him to escape were one to 10,000, and not even that; but it was never intended that he should be captured. It was his blood the bloody wretches were after, blood that would bring money in the official market of Missouri.

And this great commonwealth leagued with a lot of self-confessed robbers, highwaymen and prostitutes, to have one of its citizens assassinated, before it was positively known that he had ever committed a single crime worthy of death.

Of course everything that can be said about the dead man to justify the manner of his killing will be said; but who is saying it? Those with the blood of Jesse James on their guilty souls. Those who conspired to murder him. Those who wanted the reward and would invent any lie, or concoct any diabolical story to get it. They have succeeded, but such a cry of horror and indignation at the infernal deed is even now thundering over the land that if a single one of the miserable assassins had either manhood, conscience, or courage, he would go as another Judas and hang himself. But so sure as God reigns, there never was a dollar of blood money yet obtained which did not bring with it perdition. Sooner or later there comes a day of vengeance. Some among the murderers were mere beasts of prey. These, of course, can only suffer through cold blood, hunger, or thirst; but whatever they dread most, that will happen. Others, again, among the murderers are sanctimonious devils, who plead the honor of the State, the value of law and order, the splendid courage required to shoot an unarmed man in the back of the head; and these will be stripped to their skins of all their pretensions, and made to shiver and freeze, splotched as they are and spotted and piebald as they are with blood, in the pitiless storm of public contempt and condemnation. This to the leader will be worse than death.

Nor is the end yet. If Jesse James had been hunted

down as any other criminal, and killed when trying to escape or in resisting arrest, not a word would have been said to the contrary. He had sinned and he had suffered. In his death the majesty of the law would have been vindicated; but here the law itself becomes a murderer. It leagues with murderers. It hires murderers. It aids and abets murderers. It borrows money to pay and reward murderers. It promises immunity and protection of murderers. It is itself a murderer—the most abject, the most infamous, the most cowardly ever known to history. Therefore these so-called executors of the law are outlaws. Therefore, let Jesse James' comrades—and he has a few remaining worth all the Fords and Liddils that can be packed together between St. Louis and St. Joseph—do unto them as they did unto him. Yes, the end is not yet nor should it be. The man put a price upon his head and hire a band of cutthroats and highwaymen to murder him for money? Anything can be told of men. The whole land is filled with liars, robbers, and assassins. Murder is easy for $100. Nothing is safe that is pure, or unsuspecting, or just; but it is not to be supposed that the law will become an ally and a co-worker in this sort of a civilization. Jesse James has been murdered, first, because an immense price had been set on his head—and there isn't a low-lived scoundrel today in Missouri who wouldn't kill his own father for money; and second because he was made the scapegoat of every train robber, footpad, and highwayman between Iowa and Texas. Worse men a thousand times than the dead man have been hired to do this thing. The very character of the instruments chosen show the infamous nature of the work required. The hand that slew him had to be a traitor's. Into all the warp and woof of the devil's work there were threads woven by the fingers of a harlot. What a spectacle! Missouri with splendid regiments and militia. Missouri with 117 sheriffs, as brave and as efficient on the average as any men on earth. Missouri, with a watchful and vigilant marshal in every one of her principal towns and cities. Missouri, with every screw, and cog, and crank, and lever, and wheel of her administrative machinery in perfect working order. Boasting of law, order, progress, and development, had yet to surrender all these in the face of a single man—a hunted, lied-upon, proscribed, and outlawed man, trapped and located in the midst of 35,000 people, and ally with some five or six cutthroats and prostitutes that the majesty of the law might be vindicated, and the good name of the State saved from further reproach! Saved. Why, the whole State reeks today with a double orgy, that of lust and that of murder. What the men failed to do the women accomplished. Tear the two bears from the flag of Missouri. Put thereon in place of them, as more appropriate, a thief blowing out the brains of an unarmed victim; and a brazen harlot, naked to the waist and splashed to the brows in blood.

In the wake of such explosive oratory it was no wonder that the Ford boys were looked upon with disfavor. Certainly the country did not ring with praises of the men who had brought the outlaw down. Instead, one of the most popular ballads of the day, and for years afterward, contained these words:

> And the dirty little coward
> Who shot Mister Howard
> Has laid Jesse James
> In his grave.

Zee James returned to St. Joseph after the funeral and on April 8 offered her household effects (and one pistol) to be sold at auction. A large crowd of relic hunters paid two hundred dollars for worthless furniture: five dollars for the rickety husk-bottom chair on which Jesse had been standing at the moment of the fatal shot. An old valise said to have carried the loot of several robberies brought twenty-four dollars. A small revolver sold for twenty-five dollars. Somebody paid fifteen dollars for the little pup that Jesse had carried on his saddle between Kearney and St. Joseph as a present for his seven-year-old son. Souvenir collectors even ripped off pieces of the house and planks from the fence, and they considered themselves richer by such acquisitions. At the end of the day it was discovered that two cartridge belts had been stolen.

A long time afterward Jesse's widow presented the governor's son, T. T. Crittenden, Jr., with the gun which Jesse had placed on the bed a minute before his death. It is a Smith &

Wesson (Schofield's Model), .45 caliber, Serial No. 366, year 1873. On the right side is scratched "Laura," said to be the name of an early sweetheart of Jesse's.

By this time Jesse James had become more than ever a legendary character, and many Missourians glorified his exploits and sang his praises. However, the newspapers did what they could to offset the sentimental attitude.

The Carrollton (Missouri) *Democrat* said:

> The *Democrat* has no sympathy with the maudlin sentimentality being indulged in by certain papers over the manner of Jesse James' taking off. True, a pistol was not placed in his hands and he was not told to "defend himself." It is also true that his wife is heartbroken, her children orphaned, and his aged mother bowed down with grief. The style of Jesse's killing, however, was one peculiar to himself and followed by him successfully for years, as his scores of victims witness. Jesse also had made widows—women whose husbands have been shot down in cold blood like dogs; nor did he ask them to place themselves upon the defense. The weeds of mourning now worn by Mrs. Westfall of Plattsburg, and Mrs. Captain Sheets of Gallatin; the helpless and orphaned children of these and dozens of other families in Missouri and elsewhere and the wails of mothers all over the land for the cruelly murdered sons come up as a rebuke to the disgusting expression of regret for James' death. True, his wife and children, his mother and other innocent relatives are to be pitied for their unfortunate connection with such a man, but as for him or the manner of his death, we can and do have none. He was killed for money; but Jesse has taken scores of lives, either one of whom was worth tenfold more than his, for the same object. His hands reek with the gore of good and brave men who were mercilessly shot down while in the peaceful discharge of their business vocations, that he might rob their pocketbooks, possess themselves of their rings and watches; nor did he stop to consider tears of widows, the wails of mothers; or anguish or helplessness of orphans; nor did he care for any or all of these things. Money he wanted and human blood in his estimation was cheap and worthless. Well would it have

been for this State if some Bob Ford had sent a bullet through his brain years ago.

The following is taken from the Independence (Missouri) *Sentinel*:

Missourians who think more of Missouri and its prosperity than they do of outlaws, thieves, murderers, need not be disturbed by the silly twaddle of certain sentimental fools in other states over the killing of Jesse James. The most important and satisfactory reflection with all true Missourians is that Jesse has been put where he can commit no more murder nor rob any more trains. In securing a man who can rid the country of Jesse James we outspokenly applaud the method employed by Crittenden, Craig, and Timberlake, because, first, it was cheap; second, it was expeditious; and third, it was successful.

The New York *Herald* went into the matter at great length:

The Chicago *Times* says Mrs. Jesse James relates the following story of her husband's career as a bandit: Mrs. James is the daughter of highly respected parents, who have lived in or near Kansas City for over thirty years, and, as she remarked, she had lived there "ever since she could remember, until she married Jesse." Their courtship was a highly romantic one. They were first cousins, and their betrothal was bitterly opposed by her folks. She was sentimental, however, and expressed her determination to follow Jesse's fortunes wherever they might lead, and to prevent an elopement the old people consented to the engagement. They were married at Kearney, Mo., just after Jesse had been made an outlaw under the civil code, and a price set upon his person. Their courtship lasted five years, during which time Jesse frequently visited his inamorata at the residence of her parents in that city, and she several times went to his mother's, Mrs. Samuel, at Kearney, to see him by appointment.

During one of these visits the two were together in the yard at the Samuel residence when a party of five men, led by one of Pinkerton's detectives, went to the house, and all the time they were searching the place Jesse lay on the ground while his affianced was secreted in a fence corner. Mrs. James says that Jesse has frequently said since that if he had killed a couple of these men it might have saved his stepbrother's life and his mother's arm, but he refrained because he was afraid his sweetheart might be injured in the melee. The month following their marriage they went to Sherman, Texas, where a sister of Jesse lives.

Mrs. James took occasion to denounce the reported estimate of Jesse's stealings, which, if true, would have made him a rich man at his death. She declares that so far from having had at any time $600,000 he never had that sum in all his life, putting every cent into the calculation. They spent the money from the Gads Hill robbery on their Texas honeymoon. Things grew hot in Sherman, and they moved to Dallas in September, where they remained until the winter of 1874-75, when Mrs. James returned to Kansas City and visited her sister, Mrs. McBride, and other relatives for several months, while Jesse went on a scout. It was about this time that the Corinth, Mississippi, and Muncie, Kansas, robberies were committed, in both of which Jesse participated.

After giving an account of several robberies and how her husband and she moved about to Nashville, Baltimore, and other places to evade the officers of justice, she said she did not attempt to defend her husband's crimes, but declared that he was charged with a thousand offenses he never committed. Of Jesse's dress she says that he and his brother were always tasty and inclined to be stylish in their attire, but that Jesse never wore a frock coat, as he was said to have done while living here. His coat was short, and for that reason he usually carried but one revolver when on the street to prevent its being noticed. His arms she now has carefully stowed away where no one can see them. When asked about Frank and others of the old party she declared she did not know; that Frank was at their house once or twice during their residence in Tennessee, but she had not seen him for two years. The others, with the exception of the Hite brothers, who were her cousins, and Dick Liddil, she never saw in her life.

Chapter 22

Time had dulled much of the hatred in the border states, and the James boys had become regarded as outlaws rather than Rebels.

The murder of Jesse brought his whole life back into prominence, and people began to see him again as the boy misled by circumstance.

In the Western states, a good deal of importance had always been placed on the way a man died. To be shot in a fair fight was a sad but honorable thing; to be bushwhacked was a crime. To kill for a cause could be excused, but to kill for money was vile.

Governor Crittenden was the first to feel the impact of Jesse's death. He had condoned the murder because the railroad interests demanded it, and because Eastern bankers refused to invest money in Missouri while the James gang was riding. He had the state foremost in his mind, and Jesse's death brought about an increase in railroad business which netted the state of Missouri $3,090,000. It can be argued that the citizens should have been pleased, but this would have been a denial of the Westerner's sense of honor. He looked upon this as blood money.

As a politician, Crittenden was ruined. He had been groomed for national office, and there was talk of possibly running him for the Presidency. His implication in Jesse's death brought about a steady decline in his popularity and after defeat at the polls, he was forced into private life.

Police Commissioner Craig, realizing that he had leaped upon the wrong bandwagon, tried to explain away his part in the plot; but the voters had already labeled him, and he was not re-elected.

The public seemed to feel that Sheriff Timberlake was simply doing his job, and he retained his office for many years.

There was naturally a great deal of talk that Frank James

was gathering the "James Gang" to begin a reign of terror against everyone connected with the murder of his brother. Jim Cummins went east because of such rumors. Frank had no thoughts of revenge. What had happened to Jesse was inevitable, and for the first time in his life, Frank was free to plan his own life; and he wanted peace.

Charley and Bob Ford had expected a reward of ten thousand dollars, but they had not reckoned on the deviousness of the law. In a book about his father (*My Father, Jesse James:* Frederick Fell, New York), Jesse James, Jr., relates a meeting he and his grandmother, Mrs. Samuel, had with Charley a year after the killing. It was in Kansas City and Jesse, Jr., was eight years old. They passed Ford on the street and Mrs. Samuel confronted him.

"You don't know me, Charley," she said.

Ford stopped and faced her. "Yes," he said, "I know you. You are Mrs. Samuel."

"Yes, and you killed my brave boy," she said. "You murdered him for the money. I ought to kill you myself!"

Charley covered his face with his hands. "Please don't say that, Mrs. Samuel," he blurted. "If you only knew what I am suffering, you wouldn't talk like that."

"And what have you made me and mine suffer?"

"Mrs. Samuel, I have lived in hell since it was done. But I didn't kill him. It was Bob did it."

"Yes, and you knew Bob intended to do it when you brought him to my house. You ate bread under my roof with murder in your hearts, and murder for money, too." She asked him what he had done with his share of the ten thousand dollars.

"Mrs. Samuel, before God, we never got but a few hundred dollars of that money," Charley said.

The truth of Charley's statement is apparent in the fact that the two brothers were broke soon after the killing, and had to find a way to earn their living.

They tried to reap a harvest from their vast publicity by touring with a play called *How I Killed Jesse James*, under the auspices of the showman George H. Bunnell. They were presented for one week at the corner of Broadway and Ninth Street in New York City beginning on Monday, September 18, 1882, then on September 25 opened at Mr. Bunnell's Museum at Court and Remsen streets in Brooklyn, New York.

In the East they were received fairly well, but in the Midwestern states and in the West they were booed off the boards. Several times they had to be spirited through a back door to avoid an unfriendly mob. One night while they were performing at the Théâtre Comique in Kansas City, it was rumored that Frank James was going to kill them. Commissioner Craig and Sheriff Timberlake rushed police reserves to the scene, but nothing happened. Actually Frank James was in the audience that night, but nobody recognized him.

On May 6, 1884, Charley Ford committed suicide in his father's home near Richmond, Missouri.* Dick Liddil had to get far away, so he went to Cincinnati, Ohio, and found employment as a stable hand. In 1893, he died a natural death.

---

* His ten-year-old nephew, Tom Jacobs, and the father of former Governor Forrest Smith of Missouri helped to place the body on the bed.

Chapter 23

Bob Ford went to Las Vegas, New Mexico, and opened a saloon. He later went to Walsenburg, Colorado, where he operated a saloon-gambling hall. Eventually he arrived in Pueblo, Colorado, and opened a fancy honkytonk in a section known as The Mesa. There was a clubhouse near the police station where he made friends among the barflies.

Edward O'Kelley, a member of the city police force in Pueblo, hated Bob Ford for his killing of Jesse James, and he was outspoken about it, especially when he was drunk. In 1889 Ford beat O'Kelley to the draw and could have killed him then and there, but too many of O'Kelley's whisky-nose friends were around. Ford whacked O'Kelley over the head with his pistol and knocked him unconscious, then stooped over, picked up Ed's own gun and left the saloon.

This incident was a partial springboard for Ed's later killing of Ford. Some have claimed that Bob Ford and O'Kelley shared a room and quarreled over a diamond ring that Bob accused Ed of stealing. Others took a more fantastic stand, saying that Bob's death was the result of a Missouri vendetta. It was even said that O'Kelley killed Ford in a quarrel over a girl, but O'Kelley had never cared for any woman in his entire life. This was confirmed by his own brother, Dr. Frank O'Kelley, a Missouri resident who long fought for Ed's release from the penitentiary.

In September, 1891, Ed got drunk while on duty and shot an unarmed colored man on what is now First Street. The authorities held him in jail until the old Negro recovered, and if Ed hadn't been a member of the police force he would have been sent to prison then, but they wanted to hush it up. The official report read that O'Kelley was discharged from the Pueblo police force for being drunk on the job; nothing was ever mentioned of his shooting the Negro.

Without a job, O'Kelley wandered around Pueblo, frequenting the Turf Exchange gambling house south of the river and the Green Light House north of the river. He was in the habit of wearing his old police uniform with the brass buttons cut off. Most of the time he was drunk or mooching handouts from gamblers around the town.

When the big rush for the mining camp of Creede, Colorado, started, O'Kelley went with the crowd, and Bob Ford did also. Creede, merely the depot and post office at the end of the Denver & Rio Grande narrow-gauge railroad, was a mile away from Jimtown, which was only five blocks long with one street in a gulch five hundred feet wide.

Another actor in the Ford-O'Kelley drama was Jefferson Randolph (Soapy) Smith. He earned his nickname because he would take a piece of common brown soap the size of a French fried potato, wrap a ten-dollar or twenty-dollar bill around it, then wrap the same in a pink paper, before dropping it into a derby hat. There never was any money in the package taken from the hat, for Soapy was a sleight-of-hand artist. The suckers fell hard for the trick, and it cost them a dollar each to look at the package in the hat.

Slippery Soapy Smith found that in Jimtown there was no interference with his vocation, for nobody knew where the county lines were and therefore nobody had jurisdiction. He took over the town, appointing his brother-in-law, John Light, as marshal. Smith owned and operated the Orleans Club on the east side of the canyon, and woe betide any sucker who thought he had a chance to win anything in Soapy's place. It was common knowledge that every game in the place was fixed. There was faro bank, bird cage, roulette, chuck-a-luck and stud poker, all as crooked as a ram's horn. Soapy was able to feed all his dealers and shills because he had a cook and a couple of helpers in the kitchen.

The other two gambling emporiums in Jimtown were Ford's Omaha Club and the Gunnison Club and Exchange. Smith wanted the other owners to accept his own methods, but they refused to go along with his proposition. The Smith gang went to work on the Gunnison place first. Each night they would go into the place as gamblers and then start a row. Eventually there was the killing of Red McCune, one of the owners, who always tended bar. However, in the case of Bob Ford the Smith gang were afraid to start anything because they knew he was a dead shot and fast on the draw, not afraid of anything. Consequently they confined their activities to sending him letters written in chicken blood. These warning letters, signed "Committee," warned that if Ford did not close up and get out of town he would be given the same treatment he had given Jesse James.

One night Ford got liquored up, leaped on his pony, and rode up and down the street. He stopped in front of the free-and-easy house referred to as the Central Theatre. There he made a speech to a crowd, telling them that there was a certain element in town writing him unsigned letters and threatening to bump him off. Ford said that if there was any one man in town who cared to shoot it out with him, he would be happy to oblige. He would meet anyone interested on The Mesa (west of the lower part of Jimtown). By that time the first electric lights had come to Amethyst Street; Ford pulled out his gun and shot out a light some fifty feet away, as a demonstration of his skill. After this Smith realized that Ford was a dangerous man to fool around with.

Soapy Smith was smart enough to get someone to do his killings for him. Around his saloon Edward O'Kelley regularly looked for free drinks or odd jobs, and Smith picked him as a likely prospect, since he knew of O'Kelley's hatred for Ford. Smith reminded O'Kelley of the way he had shot the colored man in Pueblo, then told him he had nothing to fear about killing Ford, since everything would be fixed.

"You'll become world-known as the man who killed the man who killed Jesse James!" he promised.

There was another curious character in Jimtown who played a minor role in the drama. This man was an under-sized French Canuck named Joe Duval. He was a booze hound and never did any kind of work, at least not that anyone knew about. He came into town each morning on his little donkey and went from saloon to saloon to see if anyone would treat him. His attempt to speak English was so comical that it usually earned him a free drink.

A big fire had emptied Willow Gulch of all its buildings. However, some of the wiser inhabitants had erected structures south of Jimtown on what was known as the School Land, which is the present site of Creede, Colorado. Shortly after the fire Bob Ford secured a location on the School Land and had a floor put down. He erected a tent over the flooring, and this was to serve as a temporary saloon. His bartender, on a visit to his mother in Kansas City, did not return in time for the opening, so Ford tended bar himself.

The morning of June 8, 1892, was chilly but clear. Ford was alone in the canvas-covered saloon, cleaning up the place. The Smith gang was aware of it, and they encouraged Ed O'Kelley to saunter out into the street with a sawed-off shotgun under his coat. Seeing old Joe Duval, Ed called him over and asked him to have a drink. Together they walked to Ford's place, and O'Kelley shoved Duval through the doorway ahead of him. When Bob turned his head to see who was coming, O'Kelley let him have it with both barrels, shooting him in the throat and almost taking off his head. Ford's collar button was later found embedded in a pole supporting the tent, and Soapy Smith carried it for the rest of his life as a good-luck charm.

Ford's saloon was only three hundred feet from Vidil's log-building restaurant, where at the time Norval Jennings was working as a dishwasher for eight dollars a week. He was at the tent saloon when Ford's body was carried from behind the bar.

Marshal John Light suddenly appeared on the spot, as prearranged, and he took O'Kelley in tow in order to keep him from being mobbed and lynched. It was very bad medicine in those days to shoot down an unarmed man. Ford's six-gun had been on the back bar, but he had not gotten a chance to use it. He always remained unarmed when in the saloon, although he invariably carried a weapon when walking or riding around town. Marshal Light took both O'Kelley and Duval to Del Norte in Rio Grande County and turned them over to the sheriff. Even there the people wanted to lynch O'Kelley when they learned how Ford had come to his end. Oddly enough, Ford's manner of demise aroused as much condemnation of his killer as his own killing of Jesse James had brought upon himself.

Although Soapy Smith had managed to be in Denver the day of the murder, he knew that O'Kelley had merely obeyed his instructions, so he kept his promise to the extent of furnishing legal aid for O'Kelley. The trial took place in Lake City on July 12, 1892, and O'Kelley was sentenced to life imprisonment at the Canon City Penitentiary, with ten days of each year in the dungeon. Joe Duval was given two years. Soapy Smith was quite a politician in Colorado, and soon the gears were working to get O'Kelley released. By 1902 he was a free man again, largely owing to the efforts of his younger brother, Frank, as well as to the political wheels put in motion before Soapy Smith left Creede.

Bob Ford was buried up on The Mesa south of the School Land. Norval Jennings reports that there was quite a large funeral, with a procession winding its way up the side of the hill. Ford's body was later exhumed and reburied at Richmond, Ray County, Missouri, near the grave occupied by the body of his brother Charley. (Dot Evans Ford, Bob's wife, committed suicide at Durango, Colorado, on June 16, 1902.)

The finale to the Bob Ford drama occurred on January 13, 1904, when O'Kelley was in Oklahoma City, drunk and bragging. He spent several nights sleeping in a railroad depot, but when the station agent noticed this was becoming a habit, he called the police to remove him. The officer who answered the call was Joe Burnett, a quarter-breed Cherokee Indian. Joe neglected to search O'Kelley before leading him out, and Ed pulled a gun on him. In the ensuing struggle O'Kelley was killed. He was buried in the Oklahoma City potter's field, unmourned and without rites.

The newspapermen who invaded Jimtown when Ford was shot failed to get an accurate report, intentionally or not. Of course, they wanted to whet the palates of their readers, so some of them wrote that Ford was killed by direct order of Frank James. Odd, too, that the many reports varied so greatly in detail, even to the spelling of O'Kelley's name—Ed Kelly or Ed O. Kelly—but Ed signed the prison blotter as Edward O'Kelley.

Soapy and his crew left Jimtown soon after the death of Ford and went to the Klondike to join the gold rush. At Skagway, it is said, they netted more than a million dollars in gold from their various types of robbery. Soapy met his end at the hands of Frank Reid, an honest citizen who had vowed to run Smith out of Skagway or die in the attempt. In July, 1898, the two men met on a wharf at Skagway—Soapy armed with a .44-.40 Winchester, Reid with a six-shooter. Smith was killed by a bullet through the heart, while Reid was wounded so seriously that he died twelve days after the duel. Today Smith's grave is a tourist attraction at Skagway, but Reid's grave is seldom asked about.

Chapter 24

The death of Jesse James, accompanied by the treachery of several gang members, unnerved Frank James to such an extent that he at once considered surrendering to Governor Crittenden, with the understanding that he would be granted a fair trial for alleged crimes. He traveled to Jefferson City, Missouri, where he met Major John Newman Edwards at the St. James Hotel, and there he unfolded his plans. He professed to be entirely through with outlawry and anxious to settle down and forget his past.

Major Edwards told Frank James that his many friends would back him. After the secret interview Frank remained in seclusion for a time at St. Louis, where a purse of more than five thousand dollars was raised to secure his pardon. However, Governor Crittenden explained that it would not be in order for him to offer Frank James a pardon in advance of his surrender and possible conviction.

On June 2, 1882, a meeting was held in Jefferson City, and plans for Frank's surrender seemed to be clear. However, friends of Frank and officials of Clay County jumped the gun and so caused a delay in the arrangements. They sent Mrs. Zerelda Samuel and Mrs. Frank James, together with Commissioner Henry Craig and an attorney, to the capital city to open negotiations with the governor's representative. Frank James had been entrusting the whole matter to Major Edwards and did not know that his wife and mother were interfering like this.

Mrs. Samuel stormed and created quite a scene. She demanded that the governor give Frank an unconditional pardon immediately and made threats if anyone should harm him. Of course, the governor refused to heed her ravings, and she had to return to Kearney unsatisfied. When she ranted and foamed at Frank, he swore vengeance against the Fords before he would surrender, and things were back to where they had been before the negotiations began. To make things worse, the Brookfield, Missouri, bank was robbed that very month. Many believed Frank had a hand in this, but this robbery was actually committed by the Frank Mason gang, all of whom were soon apprehended, tried and sentenced to long prison terms.

Toward the end of June, Frank traveled east and caught a steamer bound for Australia. Many people speculated on his reasons for skipping the country and leaving his family at the Samuel home. But soon he returned and at once contacted Major Edwards at Sedalia, asking him to reopen the discussion. On October 1, Frank sent a lengthy letter to the governor, telling of his willingness to stand trial. In his reply of October 2, the governor stated that he was willing to accept the surrender but could make no promises. The letter ended with: "You may be innocent, or you may be guilty of all the heinous crimes charged to you. That the court will determine, as before said, and after the voice of the court is heard, then if it becomes necessary, I will decide what my action shall be."

On Thursday evening, October 5, Frank James quietly walked up the steps of the capitol building, accompanied by Major Edwards. Their meeting with the governor was brief. Frank unbuckled his belt containing a Remington .44-caliber revolver and forty-two cartridges, and said, "Governor, for the first time in twenty-one years I now permit another man to take my pistol. It is the happiest moment of my life. I feel freer, braver, and better today than I ever felt since 1861. If you will, I would like for you to keep this pistol and belt as a gift from me. Each has a history. One day, if I am spared, I will give it to you as truthfully as I can recall it. That belt was captured in open fight at Centralia. That pistol, after its owner had shot me through and through, was taken from him before I fell. I am now unarmed and your prisoner. I have trusted you as I have never trusted any other man. Do with me as you please."

The governor and his aides were touched.

"You shall have every protection afforded by the laws of your country, and as fair a trial as though you were the son of a President," replied Governor Crittenden.

It was at once arranged for Frank James to leave Jefferson City at midnight and to travel to Independence in the company of the governor's secretary, F. C. Farr, there to be turned over to the civil authorities of Jackson County. After a half-hour's talk with reporters and capitol building personnel, Frank James went to the McCarty House, where nearly a thousand persons came to shake his hand. They found him soft-spoken and friendly, a man with seventeen bullet scars, thinning hair and great physical endurance, though slender and having a tired and worn look.

To one reporter he said, "I am tired of an outlaw's life. I have been hunted for twenty-one years. I have literally lived in the saddle. I have never known a day of perfect peace. It was one long, anxious, inexorable, eternal vigil. When I slept it was literally in the midst of an arsenal. If I heard dogs bark more fiercely than usual, or if I heard the feet of horses in a greater volume than usual, I stood to my arms. Have you any idea what a man must endure who leads such a life? No, you haven't. No one can understand unless he has lived it for himself."

On Friday morning Frank James arrived in Independence, where a large crowd of excited citizens tried to grasp his hand. The outlaw's young son and wife were there to greet him, and the public were glad to see their happy embraces. The officials who met Frank at the railroad depot were Commissioner Craig, Prosecuting Attorney Wallace and Marshal Murphy, the last carrying the warrants which charged Frank James with the murder of Pinkerton Agent Whicher and the holdup and murder connected with the Winston and Blue Cut train robberies. Frank was first taken to the courthouse; then in the afternoon he was removed to a comfortable cell in the jail.

To the jailor, Mr. Holland, Frank said, "I have come to stay a while. All I ask is fair treatment and a fair trial."

During the days that followed Frank had his preliminary hearing before Judge H. P. White of the Criminal Court of Jackson County, and many prominent farmers talked of posting a bond for the noted bandit. Among those eager to assist were Colonel A. H. Powell, a prominent banker of Lee's Summit, and Bob Hudspeth, a wealthy farmer of Jackson County. They agreed to post a hundred-thousand-dollar bond if necessary, especially after it was learned that still another indictment was pending against Frank—for the killing of Cashier Sheets during the robbery of the bank in Gallatin, Daviess County, Missouri.

Frank remained in the Independence jail until his trial

opened at Gallatin on August 21. Jailor Holland eventually lost his job for being too lenient with the outlaw in allowing him the run of the place.

The authorities had agreed to hold Frank's trial at Gallatin because they thought that, aside from the holdup of the Gallatin Bank, the strongest case against the defendant was the one charging him with participation in the robbery of the Rock Island train at Winston, which was just west of Gallatin. In that robbery, you will remember, two murders were committed: William Westfall, the conductor, and Frank McMillen, the stonemason. Proof of Frank's presence at that time could have cost him his life.

Defending Frank James were some of the best legal talent in the country: Judge John F. Philips of Kansas City, James H. Slover, John M. Glover, Christopher T. Garner, Joshua W. Alexander, Charles P. Johnson and William H. Rush. The prosecution was conducted by William H. Wallace of Jackson County with the help of William D. Hamilton of Gallatin, John H. Shanklin (president of the Missouri Bar Association), Marcus A. Low, Joshua F. Hicklin and Henry Clay McDougal (later head of the firm of McDougal and Sebree).

Before the trial William H. Wallace was in the office of the Daviess County prosecutor, William D. Hamilton, when he noticed Sheriff Crozier about to summon the jury. Crozier was standing in the courthouse yard. He would pull a paper out of his pocket, look at it, then cross the street and accost some man standing on the sidewalk. Then he would come back to the courthouse yard, take the paper out of his pocket again, and go through the same performance.

Wallace walked up to the sheriff and told him he was satisfied they were going to have a fixed jury.

Crozier asked innocently, "What makes you think that?"

Wallace informed him that he had been watching him pick the jury.

Wallace then conferred with Hamilton, and they agreed to sign an affidavit alleging improper conduct on the part of the sheriff, and to ask that Coroner Claggett be directed to summon an impartial jury from the country people. Some objections were raised, since Mr. Claggett was an ex-Confederate soldier and, oddly enough, the defense did not want an ex-Confederate to pick the jury. The air was full of threats of violence.

On hearing of the intention of Hamilton and Wallace,

Judge C. H. S. Goodman asked, "Do you intend to replace Sheriff Crozier for the selection of the jury?"

Wallace replied, "Yes. Justice is being cheated."

The judge then said, "Gentlemen, I am not in the habit of announcing my decision beforehand, but if you will make such a motion I will certainly overrule it in order to prevent bloodshed."

Wallace then threatened to give up and go home, but he was prevailed upon to stick with Hamilton and the other prosecuting attorneys, since it was he who knew most about the case.

He said, "Very well. If you put it on that ground I will stay. But bear in mind that we will simply be trying Frank James before the world, for the jury's verdict is already written."

Altogether the state called nineteen witnesses and sixteen appeared for the defense. None of them ever mentioned having seen a saber cut (such as was on Frank's face) on any of the bandits, even though at the Winston holdup the bandits had been unmasked. The closest to an accusation came from people who claimed to have seen Frank near the place of the robbery a month before it was perpetrated.

The first week of the trial was consumed by Dick Liddil's evidence and cross examinations. He was led to admit that he had served a penitentiary term for horse stealing and had been pardoned upon promising to testify against Frank James. The defense attorneys gave him "the most terrific arraignment of a witness ever made in Missouri," according to the Honorable John T. Barker years later. In the course of this, in fact, Philips said to the court:

> For fifty years the British government, from which comes our noble heritage of common law and civil institutions, has suffered no citizen of that realm to be convicted on the uncorroborated testimony of an admitted accomplice in crime. How desperate must be the cause of the state when it resorts to such a witness! You, gentlemen of the jury, have never met with such a constellation of atrocities in any one man as this fellow represents. He comes from jail in Alabama to taint the sanctuary of justice with his false breath, reeking with treachery to the offices of friendship and hospitality. He should never have been permitted to pollute the Bible by

taking the oath on the Book. He should have been sworn on the knife, the dagger, proper symbols of his profession.

Liddil was questioned at length but stood the fire well and answered without flinching. He had to talk about the Glendale robbery and about the arrest and imprisonment of Whisky-Head Ryan. Many incidents in the lives of the James brothers were combed back and forth. Liddil refused to tell some things about himself, and his memory seemed clouded as to some facts that he should have readily known. It appeared to many that he was trying rather to befriend Frank than to help the prosecution, as he was supposed to be doing. The prosecuting attorney even made a motion to strike Liddil's testimony from the record, but this was overruled by the Court.

Toward the end of the first week J. T. Ford and his sons Bob and Charley took the stand, but their testimony was of no value to either side. They talked about Wood Hite's killing, but all evidence concerning the murder was considered irrelevant and therefore ruled out. Elias (Capline) Ford and Mrs. Martha Bolton were two others who contributed nothing.

General Jo Shelby had been subpoenaed, obviously against his will, and his appearance caused considerable stir in the courtroom. He announced, "I have not seen Frank James since 1872. Your Honor, may I have your permission to shake hands with an old soldier?"

The Court replied definitely, "No, you have not my permission!"

During his cross examination by Wallace, Shelby complained of that attorney's attitude, asking, "Your Honor, is it permissible for a lawyer to insult an unarmed man who is a witness?" But the questions were allowed to be continued.

As Shelby stepped down from the witness stand, he nodded to the defendant, saying, "God bless you, old fellow."

The judge took him to account for the breach of court etiquette, demanding, "Do you claim immunity on the grounds of ignorance?"

"No, sir," replied Shelby. "I have never sailed under that flag."

He was fined ten dollars for contempt of court and allowed to leave the courtroom.

Squire Earthman, the man who had assisted in capturing Ryan, was examined, and after him came to the stand George Hall, a neighbor of General Shelby. But none of them had anything to say that could help the prosecution.

In summing up for the defendant, Colonel Philips gave a long and arduous speech, ending with:

> To convinct this man because some town politician or public clamor demands it, would not only be cowardice but judicial murder. The men who cry out for the life of the so-called outlaw, no matter what the proof or the law, are themselves outlaws and demons. No, gentlemen of the jury, this courthouse iṣ the temple of justice. The voice of clamor, the breath of prejudice, must not enter here. You are sworn sentinels on guard at its portals. Do your duty. Stand, and forever, on your oaths. Remember that, after all, the true heroes of this world are its mortal heroes. The Aztec who can tear out his heart and fling it, while still palpitating, as an offering to his god, is simply an untaught barbarian. The soldier who can march up to the cannon's mouth, the fireman who can mount his ladder wreathed in flames and go to the rescue of human life, exhibit splendid courage. The man who can die for truth, or face the frowning, mad, unappeasable multitude and stand immovable for the right, is grander and braver than all others.
>
> Free men of Daviess County, let it not be said of your verdict that law and personal freedom have, in their march across the centuries, lost one atom of their vigor, or virtue, by being transplanted in American soil. Be brave and manly. If you err, let it be on the side of mercy. It is Godlike to be merciful; it is hellish to be revengeful. "I will have mercy and not sacrifice," said the Saviour when on earth. Let your verdict be a loyal response to the evidence and the spirit of the law; and as true manhood ever wins tribute, when the passion of the day is past, and reason has asserted her dominion, you will be honored and crowned.

At noon on September 6, 1883, Prosecutor Wallace completed the state's argument with a speech which would have done credit to any orator:

I can only say that on the border of our state, where the red lightning of murder played the fiercest along the western sky and the dogs of war were turned loose on defenseless women and children, I saw it all. When torch and fire and sword and rapine and pillage and plunder and robbery and murder and assassination were abroad in the land; when sabered horsemen shot across the prairies and devouring flames leaped from farm to farm and house to house, until both earth and sky seemed ablaze with living horrors, I saw it all, and, like a vast panorama, it rolls before me as I speak. I can only say that when almost the last vestige of property was swept from our house, a gentleman who wore the same epaulets that Colonel Philips wore and fought beneath Colonel Philip's flag, issued a cruel order by which we were denied even the poor privilege of dwelling as paupers under the old family roof.

His classic ended:

As to the theory that the James band went to marauding out of a spirit of revenge for wrongs done them at the close of the war, the jury will find that in every depredation committed money was the object. For every drop of blood shed by them a red dollar entered the pockets of the outlaws. Concerning Colonel Philips's disposition to connect their record with that of the Confederacy, it is surprising that such an insinuation does not bring the dead Confederate heroes to earth exclaiming, "No, we have no part or parcel in this!"

Why unfurl the Confederate flag at this time? Why put an insult on the men who bore it and the men who fell beneath it? Was there any justice in unfurling it here to smirch it with the innocent blood of McMillen [McCulloch] and Westfall or to roll up in its folds the ill-gotten gains of train robbers? These robbers have turned immigration past our doors and made us the subject of jeers and scoffs; that injury was nothing compared with the injury that would attend a verdict of acquittal of Frank James in the face of the overwhelming case the state has made.

It is the duty of the jury to exercise the right as God

gave them the light to see—this outlaw must be found guilty.

The courtroom fairly trembled with applause after Mr. Wallace's speech but quickly hushed as the bailiffs were directed to administer the oath to the jurors. Final instructions were given by Judge Goodman, and the jurors retired at twelve-thirty to consider their verdict. The court adjourned until four that afternoon.

It was nearly four o'clock when the bailiff was notified that the jury had reached a verdict. Everyone was surprised at such a short deliberation, especially Frank James, who now stood before the bar, as pale and impassive as he had been on the day the trial began.

The courtroom was breathless as Foreman of the Jury William T. Richardson read: "State of Missouri vs. Frank James—murder. We, the jury in the above entitled, find the defendant NOT GUILTY as charged in the indictment."

This announcement was greeted with a roar of applause from Frank's friends and counsel; others just shook their heads in disbelief and amazement. The judge declared that the two other cases against Frank James would be carried over to the October term for lack of time to try.

Frank James was thereupon arrested on a warrant for alleged participation in the Blue Cut holdup and returned to jail in Kansas City. The citizens who had promised to go bail for him did so at this time, and he was soon roaming about.

Actually there were now three indictments against Frank in Jackson County: one for the murder of Pinkerton Detective Whicher, one for the train robbery at Blue Cut, and one for the train robbery at Glendale. It would have been impossible for him to escape from such a strong case. Cornelius Murphy, who had summoned the jury that convicted Bill Ryan, was still in office and would also have picked the jury to try Frank James. However, there was doubt as to the legality of Dick Liddil's testimony because he had been in the penitentiary before joining the James gang and it was claimed he was incompetent to testify. At Gallatin Judge Goodman had overruled the objection to Liddil's testimony. But since that time Judge T. A. Sherwood of the Missouri Supreme Court, in *State* vs. *Grant*, had handed down the opinion that a witness who had been convicted of petty larceny was not competent to testify. The general opinion was that Wallace's

witness, Liddil, would also be disqualified at the next trial of
Frank James, and that is what happened. The governor refused to grant Liddil a full pardon to restore his competency,
so Wallace had to dismiss his case against Frank James.

Governor Crittenden continued to take a protective interest
in Frank, and under date of December 31, 1883, he was writing from Jefferson City:

> JUDGE ARNOLD KREKEL,
> WESTERN DISTRICT OF MISSOURI:
> MY DEAR SIR: An attempt is being made by United
> States Marshal McGee to seize Frank James under a
> capias from a Federal court in Alabama and remove
> him from this to that state. As there are one or more in-
> dictments pending against him for alleged felonies com-
> mitted within this state, he should not be removed from
> the jurisdiction of its courts until the prosecutions
> against him here have been exhausted. The jurisdiction
> of this state first attached by his arrest, and being placed
> in the custody of its law officers—being now out on bail,
> that custody has been transferred to his bailors. In sup-
> port of this view, I call your attention to case of *Taylor*,
> in 16th Wallace, which is decisive upon the point at is-
> sue. I respectfully suggest to you the propriety of advis-
> ing the marshal in reference to his duties in this case. I
> am clearly of the opinion, in the light of that case, that
> the marshal has no authority to act under the capias
> from Alabama. Should he seize or attempt to seize and
> remove James from the jurisdiction of this state, he be-
> comes a transgressor upon the rights of his bailors. I
> trust you will agree with me in the adoption of such a
> course as will preserve the peace and dignity of the
> state.

The time did come when all cases against Frank James in
Missouri seemed to go to pot. At least, if anyone was further
interested in prosecuting him for any reason, he said nothing.
And Federal Judge Krekel did not forget the Alabama requisition. In February, 1884, he caused Frank's arrest and refused him bail. He was at once hustled aboard a train and
under guard taken to Huntsville, Alabama.

The Missouri badman created quite a sensation in the
Madison County area. People from many miles around came

to the jail to see him and to ask him questions. Frank was always polite and willing to co-operate in the conversation—up to a certain point. Not until April 17 did District Attorney Day read the indictment against him in the United States Circuit Court. Some twenty witnesses were brought forward to identify him as one "who robbed the government paymaster at Muscle Shoals in 1881."

On Friday, April 18, Judge Harry Bruce instructed the jurors in a clear, fair and impartial manner, and the twelve old Confederates filed solemnly from the room. Almost immediately they returned, their faces all smiles. Their verdict was a unanimous "NOT GUILTY"—for Frank's able attorneys, Confederate hero General Leroy Walker, Richard Walker and R. B. Sloan, had done an excellent job of convincing the jury that Frank James was a misguided ex-Confederate private.

It now seemed useless for any others to attempt to get Frank James behind bars. Minnesota dropped her indictment concerning the Northfield raid like a hot potato. It would be just a waste of time; anyone could see that.

When C. M. Hubbard, editor of the St. Joseph *Herald*, happened to be visiting in Detroit, a reporter on the Detroit *Journal* interviewed him.

Q. Of course the people of Missouri generally indorse the acquittal of Frank James?

A. By no means. The verdict was a public disappointment. The people of the East have an erroneous opinion of the sentiments of the people of Missouri. Why, if you believe the comments of the Eastern press, you will be apt to get the idea that Missouri is peopled and ruled by a band of outlaws and train robbers. No state in the Union has been vilified and misrepresented as Missouri has been. If a revolting murder is commited in any quarter of the state it is heralded throughout the country as another evidence of lawlessness, and pointed to as a fresh illustration of the semi-barbarous civilization alleged to exist in Missouri. Why is not the same treatment accorded in Michigan? Murder after murder has been committed here in Detroit, and the murderers are still roaming about the country seeking fresh victims. The press outside of Michigan pay little attention to these events, and we never hear anything about an alleged reign of terror here. But let a similar affair occur in Missouri, and a majority of newspapers of the country at once make it a pretext for a tirade of abuse of Missouri and all Missouri institutions. In this way a sort of popular prejudice has been created against that state, that is as unaccountable to me as it is unjust. Take the trial of Frank James as an illustration. Nine tenths of the people of Missouri know him to be an outlaw and want him hung. But he is in the hands of the law and has the same chances that any other criminal has. His acquittal at Gallatin last week simply gave us another illustration of the weakness of our American jury system. The verdict is not in keeping with the public sentiment in Missouri or with the public estimate placed upon the evidence. The acquittal of the gang of Star Route thieves was no greater surprise to the country at large than the acquittal of the bandit was to the great majority of the people of Missouri.

Q. Was there any sincerity in his prosecution?

Q. If you could hear the curses heaped upon the heads of the attorneys for the State by the friends of Frank James you would be apt to think so. Mr. Wallace of Kansas City, who had charge of the case, is the prosecuting attorney of Jackson County, where there are indictments still pending against him, and no effort was spared on the part of Mr. Wallace and his associates to make the case strong. For months they scoured the country in all directions for testimony, and the chain of evidence they succeeded in weaving, link by link, was as strong as it was possible to make it. Jo Shelby, the champion of the bandit, even charges them with going beyond the bounds of decency and inaugurating a war of persecution. Nobody, outside of the small circle of James' friends, finds any fault with the prosecution. They made a strong case and ought to have had a different verdict.

Q. Is there any suspicion that the jury was fixed?

A. Some hints of that nature have been thrown out, but the vote of the first ballot shows that if any fixing was done at all, it was in making the panel. The jury was composed entirely of farmers, and the sheriff

who summoned them was a Union soldier, born and
reared in Pennsylvania. Judge Goodman, before
whom the case was tried, is an upright man, universally respected by men of all parties. The only sig-
nificant fact connected with the trial is that every
man on the jury was a Democrat.

Q. How do people account for the verdict?

A. There's the rub. They can't account for it. All they
can do is express their surprise and denounce it. Of
course the bandit's sympathizers endorse it as just,
but no one else does.

Q. But didn't you remark a few minutes ago that the
James gang is not a part of Missouri civilization?

A. Very true. The gang is broken up. Everybody admits
that, and the only sympathizers the James boys have
is a small remnant of the Confederate element. They
are few in number, and are in no sense of the word
representative Missourians.

Q. How about General Shelby? Don't you call him a
representative citizen?

A. By no means. God help the state if he is! Jo Shelby
was a gallant rebel cavalryman and, personally, is a
genial gentleman. Frank James fought under him,
and he has been his friend and protector ever since. I
have my own ideas about his connection with the
gang and the part he played in the reign of terror
throughout Clay, Jackson, and Lafayette counties,
and the time may come when the inside history of
the work of those outlaws will reveal the connection
of better men than Jo. Shelby with their plots and
plans. Let me give you a few facts related to me recently by a prominent lawyer of Northwest Missouri.
Some years ago there lived in Clay County, if my
memory is not at fault, an attorney whose name
sounds very similar to that of the present railroad
commissioner of Missouri. He secured the enmity of
the James gang, who threatened his life and wanted
him to leave the state. He went to Minnesota and
practiced law there. Among the baggage captured
with some of the participants of the Glendale robbery was one or two pieces belonging to the James
boys. Among their contents was found a package of
letters written to Frank James by a leading Dem-

ocratic editor of the state today. They showed that he was posted as to all their movements and was constantly in communication with them, giving them advice and warnings. The Minnesota lawyer secured those letters and, desiring to return to Missouri, wrote to the writer of them stating that unless his personal safety was guaranteed he would publish the letters. The editor replied that he would not be molested, and it was arranged to place the letters in the hands of a third person, with the understanding that in the event of any injury being done to the person or property of the lawyer by any member of the gang, they were to be published. The attorney returned to his old Missouri home and has never been molested. My informant states that the lawyer himself has admitted to him the truth of these statements. There is little doubt that Shelby and others were in sympathy with the outlaws, if not actually in league with them.

Q. And Shelby still holds a prominent place in the Democratic Party of Missouri?

A. No; that is hardly a fair statement. Shelby is a Democrat, it is true; but he can hardly be said to represent anybody but Jo Shelby. He is not an office-holder, never seeks an office, and does not even figure in the Democratic conventions. In reality he has been a good deal of a bushwhacker in the Democratic camp. He always trains with a certain wing of the old Confederate element, and he has recently declared that the Confederate wing of the party must be given the offices next year.

Chapter 25

Frank James was suffering from consumption, but he retired to his farm at Fletcher, Oklahoma, and kept his home at the old homestead in Kearney as well. He worked as a shoe salesman in Dallas, Texas, for a time, and while living at 4279 Laclede Avenue in St. Louis he was a doorkeeper at the Standard Theatre. At that time his son, Robert Frank James, was employed in the auditing department of the Wabash Railroad. Frank later teamed up with Cole Younger and operated a Wild West Show called *Hell on the Border*. Frank was always an added attraction wherever he went, and sometimes he appeared at fairs and carnivals as a race-track starter.

In September, 1897, he paid a visit to the battlefield at Centralia, Missouri, and the Columbia (Missouri) *Herald* published an article about him.

"It has been reported," said Frank, "that my brother Jesse was not at the Centralia fight, that he was sick in Carroll County at the time. This is a mistake. Jesse was there. He it was who killed the commander of the Federal troops, Major Johnson. I still have that revolver he used. The Younger boys were not at Centralia."

He took an ear of corn from the battlefield saying, "I want some sort of relic, and this is the most peaceful-looking thing I see."

"Here's another souvenir," said Adam Rodmyre of the Missouri State Militia Guard, handing him a bullet found on the field.

Frank also visited the Pleasant Grove burying ground, which is in a secluded spot away from the main road, some four miles from Centralia. It is reached through a half-cleared piece of timber and contained a number of newly-made graves as well as the unmarked graves of Frank Shepherd and Hank Williams, two guerrillas, near a great pine tree.

"I would give a hundred dollars for that tree," someone remarked.

"That would be like robbing a graveyard," Frank answered solemnly.

He was standing beside the sunken grave of his comrades with his black slouch hat in his hand.

"To this complexion we come at last," he quoted, looking down at the withered grass. "Our boys are scattered everywhere. You will find their graves in the hollows and on the hills, by the gulf, and on these prairies. Many like these have no monuments. They don't need any. They made their monuments while they lived. They left a record for daring courage that the world has not surpassed. Their sleep is just as sweet here as it would be in a beautiful city cemetery." He pinched a twig from the pine tree and walked away. "The marvel to me," he continued, "is that I am not sleeping in a place like this. What have I been spared for, when so many of my comrades were taken?"

He stopped for a short while at the farmhouse of William R. Jennings, who had helped bury the Federal dead the day after the Centralia battle.

"I felt sorry for one poor boy," said Frank. "He was hardly more than seventeen and he almost reached the woods in his attempt to escape. All the Federals had been shot in the head. So unerring was the marksmanship of the bushwhackers that frequently we would find no wounds on the soldiers' bodies until we would turn back the eyelid or look into an ear—and there would be a single little hole that brought death."

"Well," said Mr. Jennings, "I hope we'll meet in a better world than this."

"I hope so," said Frank, "where there will be no fighting."

As he turned away he went on talking: "When great big grown men with full possession of all their faculties refer to that battle as the Centralia Massacre I think they are pleading the baby act. We did not seek the fight. Johnson foolishly came out to hunt us, and he found us. Then we killed him and his men. Wouldn't he have killed every one of us if he had had the chance? What is war if it isn't to kill people for a principle? The Yankee soldiers tried to kill every one of the

Southern soldiers, and the soldiers from the South tried to kill all the Yanks—and that's all there is to it.

"We were just out there in the brush not molesting anybody when Johnson and his men came after us. We never took prisoners. We couldn't do it. How could we carry them around with us? We either killed them or turned them loose. It reminds me of Macbeth: 'Never shake thy gory locks at me; thou canst not say I did it.'

"We didn't make war on women and children. They are the only people whom I sympathize with during war. Men ought to be in the fight on one side or the other. Nor did we fight the citizens except when they had played informer. I understand one citizen was killed in Centralia in a drunken row. That ought not to have been done. The Yankees killed many more noncombatants than we did.

"We have been called guerrillas, bushwhackers, and all that. I do not know who originated the name bushwhackers, but it is a pretty good description. We lived in the brush but never fought from ambush. We always gave battle in the open. I never fought from behind cover but once. Then there were only three of us and a hundred and fifty Federals were fighting us. But we got away."

When Frank spoke softly of the mistreatment of the South he set his mouth grimly and his eyes glittered.

"Bushwhackers did some bad things," he admitted, "but they never devastated and ruined the country. When General Sherman, whom the North worships as a great Christian soldier, went on his famous march he issued orders that the country should be made so desolate that to get over it a crow would have to carry his haversack full of rations with him. We did nothing like that.

"And Order Number 11—Ewing's. I am glad General Bingham put that on immortal canvas. That is a picture that talks. That order simply ruined hundreds of peaceful homes in western Missouri. I know one man up in Jackson County who made a fortune going around picking up cattle that had been abandoned, a high-toned cattle thief."

As he moved through the woods with friends, Frank commented frequently upon the beauties of the thickets and cowpaths and wooded recesses.

"Don't that look nice? I think I would enjoy life in the woods again. For more than ten years I never slept in a bed. I had a blanket sometimes but more often nothing but the moss for a mattress and the sky for a coverlid. I think I know all the trees and shrubs of Missouri and what they are good for. I have had to use them for food and medicine sometimes, you know. Occasionally they fool me in Shaw's Garden in St. Louis with the trees and plants from other countries, but with nothing from Missouri."

That day Frank had a long talk with Colonel H. C. Threlkeld and Thomas S. Sneed, both of whom had been in Centralia at the time of the fight.

Colonel Threlkeld said, "I was only a boy, and when I came into town and saw the Federal soldiers killed at the train I backed out of town. Afterward I was starting to help put out the flames on the burning train, but I got frightened away."

Mr. Sneed said, "I did my best to persuade Johnson not to go out after Anderson, but he was in a mood to be brave and wouldn't listen to me."

Harvey Silver said, "I was watching the fight from a distance, and I saw the Federals falling dead in a space the size of a square block. They were all shot through the head. My father and I loaded nine wagons with dead bodies. We had to pile them in like logs."

"Missourians ought to vote the guerrillas a medal," said Frank James. "I know people used to call Missouri the state of bushwhackers and outlaws, the home of the James boys, where life and property were not safe. Maybe that's the reason so many emigrants went through Missouri without stopping and settled in Iowa, Kansas and Nebraska. Most of these folks were Republicans, and as a result Missouri is Democratic. Her people have been forced to depend on their own resources, and look at the result. In my own county of Clay there are fewer mortgages than in any township in Kansas. Why? Eastern money-owners refused to lend money in Missouri because the James boys came from there."

Someone asked, "How did the guerrillas live?"

Frank replied, "We usually met hospitable treatment throughout Missouri, Kentucky and states farther south. There were enough Southern sympathizers to give us a kind reception, and we had little trouble up to the last days of the war in getting enough food. We lived in the woods, of course—that was our only home. We captured from the Federals clothes, horses and ammunition. We generally carried our coats and overcoats fastened on our saddles. Most of our clothing was the blue uniform of the Yankees. We wore vests cut low in the front and trimmed with gold lace. Each guerrilla carried two to four pistols. I nearly always carried two. I was small and slender, and more than that number were too many for me.

"The stories about guerrillas riding with the reins of the horses between their teeth and firing with pistols in both hands is simply dime-novel stuff. Maybe once in a while, but mostly we always held our horses with one hand and the pistol in the other. It was as important to guide the horse as it was to hold the pistol.

"Anderson always made us keep our horses in good condition. If a man did not keep a horse and good pistols, he sent him to the infantry. I rode a horse named Little George at Centralia, and Jesse rode Ebony. At night and when we were in camp we played like schoolboys. Some of our play was as rough as football. The truth was we were nothing but great boys, anyhow.

"If you ever want to pick a company to do desperate work or to lead a forlorn hope, select young men from seventeen to twenty-one. They will go anywhere in the world you lead them. When men grow older they grow more cautious, but at that age they are regular daredevils. Take our company, and there has never been a more reckless lot of men. Only one or two were over twenty-five. Most of them were under twenty-one. Scarcely a dozen boasted a mustache. Arch Clements, who was the real brains of Anderson's command, was only twenty. He and Peyton Long and myself followed the Federals nearly to Sturgeon after Centralia. Clements was first lieutenant. He came from Kingsville, Johnson County, and he was killed at Lexington.

"There were only two of the guerrillas who would fight in a battle just like in a personal difficulty—George Todd and Dick Kinney. They would get mad in a battle just like in a fist fight. Dave Pool was a born comedian. He could have gotten five hundred a week on the stage. Up in the old German settlements of Lafayette County the mothers still quiet their children by telling them to be still or Dave Pool will get them. After the Centralia fight Pool walked across the dead bodies of the Federals, stepping from one to another. Todd asked him what he was doing. 'Counting 'em,' he said. 'But you don't need to walk on 'em to count 'em,' said Todd. 'That's inhuman.' And Pool answered, 'Well, aren't they dead? If they're dead, I can't hurt them. I can't count 'em good without stepping on 'em. When I get my foot on one this way I know I've got 'im.' Pool counted a hundred and thirty bodies in one block.

"George Wigginton, of Jackson County," Frank James continued, "was known as the man who never swore. He was a Christian if ever there was one. Very few of our men went through the war without wounds of some kind. Quite a number of the guerrillas are still living, though."

When he was asked what he considered the guerrillas' greatest raid, he said: "The greatest raid made by the guerrillas was one in September, 1864, We were north of the Missouri River only about two weeks. We had with us never to exceed two hundred and fifty men. We averaged a battle a day, and we killed over a thousand Federal soldiers besides destroying a good deal of Yankee property. The only battle in the world's history to surpass Centralia is the skirmish at Baxter Springs, Kansas, where we killed a hundred and thirty of Blunt's bodyguard.

"Yes, I was at Wilson's Creek, but that was a slow fight. The idea of that many thousand men fighting for hours and killing so few! I want results when I fight. We never met any Federal soldiers who would fight us on equal terms. They would either want to outnumber us or would run away. I have been amused to hear of the fellows in central Missouri who chased us. They always followed at a safe distance.

"The bravest Federal soldiers we met were Major Emery S. Foster's command and the Second Colorado commanded by Colonel Ford. They were fighters, sure enough. Once while this Colorado regiment was chasing us they almost reached our rear guard. Dave Pool hollered to the Yankees, 'You cowards, you, if they wasn't so many of you, I'd stop and fight you. I'd fight any one of you.' To Pool's surprise they sent out one man and called back their other troops. And then these two men, Pool and the Yankee, sat on horseback and pecked away at each other until their ammunition was exhausted. Pool had a slight flesh wound, and the other man wasn't hurt. Pool always said he would have whipped him if he hadn't been afraid of the other Federals. But we made fun of him for inviting a fight and then getting licked."

"What was your worst scare in the war, Mr. James?"

"The worst scare I ever got was during the Fayette fight. That was the only time we ever got whipped, too. Bill Anderson managed this fight. Quantrill protested against it but finally told Anderson to go and he'd fight in the ranks as a private. We charged up to a blockhouse made of railroad ties filled with portholes, and then charged back again. The blockhouse was filled with Federal troops and it was like charging a stone wall, only this wall belched forth lead.

"On a slight rise a short distance from the blockhouse one of our men, Ole Johnson, fell. When we got back our captain asked for volunteers to go after Johnson's body. Sim Whitsett and Dick Kinney and myself started out. We got to the rise all right. There we were in plain view of the Federals, and they simply peppered us with bullets. We got down as close to the ground as we could. I was mighty scared. It was the worst fight I ever had. I knew if we raised up we'd expose ourselves to the fire of the Yankees, and we couldn't stay still. I tell you, pride makes most of us do many things we wouldn't do otherwise. Many men would run away in a battle if the army wasn't watching them. Well, pride kept us there until we got Johnson's body rolled up in a blanket, and then we made tracks."

"And what was the saddest experience you ever had, Mr. James?"

The man of blood and iron told the following story with evidence of deep feeling: "I believe the saddest thing I know connected with the war occurred at the battle of Franklin, Tennessee. Young Theodore Carter was fighting there. But a few yards away was his old home with his mother standing at the window, watching the battle and waiting for him. How bravely he fought that day! With eager anticipating he looked forward to getting into his house when the battle was over—after years of absence. Almost within a stone's throw of his mother's door, within sight of the yard where he played as a boy, he was shot down and died. I visited that place some weeks ago, and since then a friend has sent me a gavel made out of the old gin house there. I cherish it for the memories it brings of that bloody day and the gallant Theodore Carter."

Judge F. Hiner Dale of Guymon, Oklahoma, has told about the biggest thrill of his boyhood, when Frank James was working in a shoe store in Nevada, Missouri, and on the side was the owner of some ranch horses which he ran at intervals. One day Frank James looked at the small boy on the sidewalk and called down from his buggy seat, "Hello, Hiner. Get in the buggy with me. I'm going over to Fort Scott, Kan-

sas, to start the races, and I don't want to go alone."
Naturally that afternoon was glorified in Hiner Dale's
memory, for he adored this wonderful Frank James.

When former President Theodore Roosevelt was running
again on the Bull Moose ticket, he, too, took a fancy to
Frank James and engaged him as his personal bodyguard.
When Quantrill's ex-guerrillas next held their annual reunion
at Wallace's Grove near Independence, Frank attended as
usual, but in the courthouse yard a dozen old-timers told him
they didn't like the way he had turned Bull Moose (that
meant to them Republican).

"After all we've been to each other, it's like you were
being a traitor now!" some of them contended.

Frank helped smooth over the situation before any fist
fights were started by saying casually, "It isn't politics, fellows. No politics in it!"

Zerelda James Samuel passed away on February 10, 1911,
in Oklahoma City, where she was carried from the train after
a stroke. She had been visiting on Frank's ranch at Fletcher
and was on her way back to Kearney. She lies buried in the
Kearney cemetery beside Dr. Samuel, who died on March 1,
1908, and beside her son Jesse Woodson James and his wife
Zee.

On February 18, 1915, when Frank died of a heart attack,
his wife Annie sobbed as she held him in her arms, "No better husband ever lived." His body was cremated with the stip-
ulation that the ashes should be placed in an urn and
deposited in a safe-deposit box, burial not to be made until
after Annie's death so that they could be buried together.
And Annie Ralston James lived near Excelsior Springs, Missouri, until she was ninety-one. She died July 6, 1944. Her
ashes were buried with those of Frank in the Elmwood Cemetery near Independence.

The principals, one by one, had left the stage, and only the
legend was left.

Jesse James became a folk hero because America was a
growing nation that needed a folklore. The development of
the West was the only phase of the nation's growth that was
uniquely American. The Eastern states had derived their cus-
toms from Europe. The industrial revolution had actually be-
gun in England. Only the West offered the basis for an
indigenous folklore, and Jesse James provided a classical example of the misunderstood badman.

He was spawned by oppression. He was loved by the people of the soil. He was daring and romantic. And his end was tragic.

There is also the fact that Jesse's death heralded the end of the Western badman. It occurred just eighteen years before the advent of the twentieth century. He was the last of the colorful desperadoes on horseback. Just twelve years after his death the automobile was in use in America. It was a mere thirty-three years between that day in St. Joseph and a day in Chicago when a new type of outlaw—Alphonse Capone—began writing a different chapter in American crime.

For the sake of the legend, Jesse James died at the right time.

ABOUT THE AUTHOR

Carl W. Breihan is a former St. Louis County Police Commissioner, Deputy Sheriff, and Deputy Marshal. Presently he is serving his third term on the St. Louis County Council. Mr. Breihan resides with his wife and daughter in a suburban area of St. Louis. He also has a son who lives in Chicago, and a married daughter whose family resides in Detroit.

Colonel Breihan is an historian of note and a universally recognized authority on the James and Younger Brothers. He knew the sons of Frank and Jesse James and Bill Doolin, as well as relatives of the Youngers. He has published fourteen books dealing with various outlaws, lawmen, and badmen of the old West, and hundreds of magazine articles. Some of his books were also published in England and in Germany. *The Day Jesse James Was Killed* was done in Braille for the Royal Academy for the Blind in London.